RACES OF MAIZE IN BOLIVIA

Ricardo Ramírez E., David H. Timothy, Efraín Díaz B.,

and U. J. Grant

in collaboration with

G. Edward Nicholson Calle, Edgar Anderson,

and William L. Brown

Publication 747

NATIONAL ACADEMY OF SCIENCES—

NATIONAL RESEARCH COUNCIL

Washington, D. C.

1960

8/12/60

COMMITTEE ON PRESERVATION OF INDIGENOUS
STRAINS OF MAIZE

OF THE

AGRICULTURAL BOARD

DIVISION OF BIOLOGY AND AGRICULTURE

NATIONAL ACADEMY OF SCIENCES — NATIONAL RESEARCH COUNCIL

Other publications in this series:

RACES OF MAIZE IN CUBA
William H. Hatheway
NAS — NRC Publication 453
1957   Price $1.50

RACES OF MAIZE IN COLOMBIA
L. M. Roberts, U. J. Grant, Ricardo Ramírez E.,
W. H. Hatheway, and D. L. Smith
in collaboration with Paul C. Mangelsdorf
NAS — NRC Publication 510   1957   Price $1.50

RACES OF MAIZE IN CENTRAL AMERICA
E. J. Wellhausen, Alejandro Fuentes O., and
Antonio Hernandez Corzo
in collaboration with Paul C. Mangelsdorf
NAS — NRC Publication 511   1957   Price $1.50

RACES OF MAIZE IN BRAZIL AND OTHER
EASTERN SOUTH AMERICAN COUNTRIES
F. G. Brieger, J. T. A. Gurgel, E. Paterniani, A. Blumenschein, and
M. R. Alleoni
NAS — NRS Publication 593   1958   Price $2.00

Previously published by the Bussey Institute, Harvard University, in 1952:

RACES OF MAIZE IN MEXICO
E. J. Wellhausen, L. M. Roberts, and E. Hernandez X.
in collaboration with Paul C. Mangelsdorf

Library of Congress Catalog Card Number: 60-60011

Price $1.50

TABLE OF CONTENTS

ACKNOWLEDGMENTS

It would be interesting to know the exact number of people who have shared in the work of making, growing, storing, assembling, and studying the collections upon which this report is based. It began as a concern of the Committee on Preservation of Indigenous Strains of Maize of the National Academy of Sciences — National Research Council in Washington, D. C. It was carried forward through the collaboration of the Bolivian and Colombian Governments, the International Cooperation Administration, and The Rockefeller Foundation. Five scientists associated with the project served without compensation other than that received from the Institutions which granted them leaves of absence for the purpose: Dr. Paul C. Mangelsdorf of Harvard University, Dr. Edgar Anderson of the Missouri Botanical Garden and Washington University, Dr. William L. Brown of the Pioneer Hi-Bred Corn Company and Washington University, Dr. Barbara McClintock of the Carnegie Institution, and Dr. G. Edward Nicholson during his tenure of a Fellowship of the Guggenheim Foundation, to name them in the order in which they were drawn into the study.

The seed storage center, maintained jointly by the Colombian Ministry of Agriculture and The Rockefeller Foundation, is located at Medellín, Colombia. Hence, the bulk of the work was done in Colombia and by Colombians. We are indebted to the directors, administrators, and staffs of the experiment stations at which this material was grown for maintenance and study. The responsibility of receiving, cataloging and storing the collections properly was borne in large part by Dr. L. M. Roberts, who also was instrumental in making many of the arrangements necessary in a study of this kind. We are extremely grateful to him for his help, encouragement, assistance, and contributions throughout the course of this study.

The following Ingenieros Agrónomos of the Corn Improvement Program of the Colombian Ministry of Agriculture deserve specific mention for their work in caring for the plants, collecting data for this report, and in the maintenance of the collections. Ing. Daniel Varela A. took notes on the highland collections grown at Tibaitatá. He also collected a large number of sporocytes for cytological study. Ings. Bertulfo Peña V. and Fernando Arboleda R. collected most of the sporocytes of the lowland material and took notes on the collections planted at Medellín. Ing. Daniel Sarria V. recorded the data on the races grown at Palmira. Ings. Libardo Escobar R. and Efraín Alvarado C. collected the data for the lowland collections at Montería. Ings. Manuel Torregroza C. and Clímaco Cassalett D. increased and maintained many of the collections previous to the time of this study. A large number of students from the Facultades de Agronomía at Medellín and Palmira assisted the Ingenieros Agronomos in note taking, summarizing data, and maintenance of the collections.

Dr. William H. Hatheway was responsible for the data on the internal characteristics of the ears and for the drawing of the cob diagrams. He also contributed in the classification of the races and has been very helpful in collecting data and sporocytes, and also for his suggestions throughout the course of the study.

Laboratory facilities for Dr. McClintock were provided by the Universidad Nacional, Facultad de Agronomía at Medellín. The bulk of the plant data were summarized by Ing. Agr. Pedro R. Oñoro C., Sr. Luis Mahecha T., Stas. Nora Rivera U. and Marina Duque B., of the Statistical Section of the Departamento de Investigacion Agropecuaria of the Colombian Ministry of Agriculture. We are indebted to Sr. Rafael Rodríguez L. for the cob diagrams and photographs of typical ears, to Sr. Terencio Rengifo H. for photographs of internode patterns, distribution maps and cob diagrams. The distribution maps were drawn by Srs. Víctor M. Pinzón R., Julio García G., Héctor H. Escobar L., and Sta. Berta Escobedo G.

We are grateful to the Chairman of the Committee on the Preservation of Indigenous Strains of Maize, Dr. R. E. Cleland; its Executive Secretary, Mr. J. Allen Clark, and to the disbursing officers of the National Academy of Sciences and The Rockefeller Foundation. Mr. Clark and the staff of the Agricultural Board of the Academy — Research Council have supervised the editing and publishing of the English edition. For the Spanish edition we are grateful to Dr. Milcíades Martínez G. and others of the publications office of the Department of Agricultural Investigations of the Colombian Ministry of Agriculture.

We are indebted to Dr. Barbara McClintock for her kind permission to use the chromosome knob data which were obtained by her. We are also grateful to Dr. Hugh C. Cutler and Ing. Alexander Grobman for their comments and suggestions.

Sr. Víctor Manuel Patiño R. served as the principal collector of Bolivian maize. Making representative collections of indigenous varieties of maize requires both agronomic and ethnographic insight, as well as the ability to deal effectively with many kinds of people. Sr. Patiño was ably assisted by Messrs. Daniel Candia, Aníbal Corro, Leandro Rojo F., Julio Romero, Teddy Monasterios, Alberto Ruíz Z., Pascual Dorado, and a number of others who made somewhat fewer but equally important collections. The outstanding abilities of these men have resulted in an unusually representative collection from a key area.

Sr. Pablo E. Daza B. has been of great assistance in receiving, cataloging, storing and maintaining the collections. He was also responsible for organizing the collections for laboratory study and taking many of the data on the internal characteristics of the ears.

Stas Eloísa Rivera E. and Elvia Quinceno A. assisted in locating records, photographs, and in typing preliminary notes on the races. We are indebted to Sta. Cecilia Cancelado S. for her exceptional typing of the first draft of the manuscript. We also wish to extend our thanks to Pauline Waddell of the Plant Breeding Department of Pioneer Hi-Bred Corn Company for typing the final drafts of the manuscript.

RACES OF MAIZE IN BOLIVIA

Ricardo Ramírez E., David H. Timothy, Efraín Díaz B., and U. J. Grant [1]

in collaboration with

G. Edward Nicholson Calle, Edgar Anderson, and William L. Brown

INTRODUCTION

This monograph of the races of maize in Bolivia grew out of a concern of the National Academy of Sciences — National Research Council that something of the great germinal diversity of maize in the New World be preserved for future generations. As was said in one of the earlier monographs in this series, Roberts, Grant, Ramírez, Hatheway and Smith (53): "Maize is the basic food plant of the Americas and its diversity, the product of thousands of years of evolution under domestication, is one of the important natural resources of this hemisphere. Losing any substantial part of that diversity may not only restrict the opportunities for future improvement, but may also increase the difficulties of coping with future climatic changes or with new diseases or insect pests."

Due to the efforts of the Committee on Preservation of Indigenous Strains of Maize, funds were obtained from the Technical Cooperation Administration (later the International Cooperation Administration). These were used to augment the cooperative program (already well under way) involving the Rockefeller Foundation and various Latin American Governments. This made it possible to make collections of indigenous varieties, to maintain them in a living condition under refrigeration and to prepare a series of monographs describing and classifying the thousands of varieties which had been brought together.

The collections of Bolivian maize were stored grown and studied at the Colombian center, at Medellín, maintained co-

[1] The authors are respectively: Co-director and Geneticist, Maize Improvement Program, Colombian Ministry of Agriculture; Associate Geneticist, Colombian Agricultural Program, The Rockefeller Foundation; Geneticist, Head of Palmira Section, Maize Improvement Program, Colombian Ministry of Agriculture; Acting Field Director, Colombian Agricultural Program, The Rockefeller Foundation.

operatively by the Colombian Ministry of Agriculture, the Rockefeller Foundation and the National Research Council. In growing,
studying, and amplifying the Bolivian collections the other Colombian experimental fields at Tibaitatá, Palmira and Montería also
played an important role.

By force of circumstances this report on Bolivian maize differs
from those on Mexican, Cuban and Colombian races. It was pre-
pared almost exclusively outside of Bolivia. It is indeed largely
a report on 844 collections of Bolivian maize as grown and studied
in Colombia. This disadvantage is somewhat compensated for by
the fact that Bolivian maize had been studied in Bolivia by Dr.
H. C. Cutler (15) over a decade earlier. His report, and the representative collections made by him, have been available to the
authors.

Due to radical changes in the pattern of maize growing in
Bolivia some of the varieties reported on here and preserved in
the "germ plasm bank" at Medellín are no longer readily obtain-
able in Bolivia. It is fortunate indeed that these studies were ini-
tiated soon enough to preserve, in a living condition, those ancient
varieties which disappeared after the Bolivian Land Reform laws
were put into effect.

VALUE OF THE MAIZE COLLECTIONS

The chief value of the Bolivian collections lies in the simple
fact that they are already irreplaceable. For hundreds of years,
conservative Bolivian landowners continued to prize the pre-
Colombian and Colonial varieties of maize to a degree probably
unparalleled elsewhere. Land reform and other social changes have
altered this pattern of land use so radically in the five years since
the Bolivian collections were made that the collections could not
be duplicated today. The "germ plasm bank" at Medellín is already becoming what it was designed to be, a repository, in the
living condition, for genes and gene combinations of *Zea mays*
which would have otherwise disappeared from cultivation. The
collection has other important values, as for instance the value of
the classification process itself. It has been found in Mexico and
Colombia, it will undoubtedly be found in Bolivia, that modern
corn breeding in these ancient centers of variability must be based

upon an understanding of the local varieties. In the Central and Eastern United States where virtually all of the commercial field corns belong to crosses between the same two races, such information is of little immediate importance. In Mexico, Colombia, or Bolivia (where there are not two races and their intermediates but a score or more of races with various intermediates) where maize is grown from sea level to over 10,000 feet, from dry to very wet climates, scientific plant breeding can scarcely begin until the racial composition of the thousands of local varieties has been approximately roughed out. It has been found in Colombia and Mexico that of the several hundred possible combinations between the different races, only a few are of possible commercial value.

In addition to the immediate practical value of the collections and their classification, to maize breeding in Bolivia and elsewhere, these collections from one of the chief variation centers of maize are basic material for research in maize breeding and in the fundamentals of genetics. It is known that when two races are crossed, the characteristics of each have a strong tendency to stay together. For differences which can be measured with such precision as chromosome knob number and position, this tendency can still be demonstrated after 50 to 100 generations of selective breeding. In the last three decades, techniques have been worked out for measuring with precision such variables as (1) Tassel branching, (2) Internode patterns, (3) Cupule size and form, (4) Knob number and position, (5) Ear and kernel characters, (6) Details of the scleric system. The time is rapidly approaching when it should be possible to combine these techniques with the methods of maize genetics much in the same manner as did Renner (51) who, by using many characters of leaf, seed and flower, was able to work out the complexes in *Oenothera* in advance of the cytological data. In maize, by the use of these characters precisely analyzed on the morphological level and then turned into quantitative measures, we should be able to follow genetically, chromosome arms or segments of chromosome arms. There is already evidence to suggest that, in lines derived from some of the varieties collected in Bolivia and in western Mexico, there are segregating complexes of characters similar to those described by

Mangelsdorf and Reeves (26) in their classic studies of maize-teosinte crosses.

For classical maize genetics, the collections provide a virtually untouched reservoir of untested genes. In time the use of this material should add to the number of gene markers of interest to genetics and may provide a source of new genes for those segments of maize chromosomes which are at present poorly marked.

Also of fundamental importance is the use that can and should be made of this material in experiments designed to shed light on the problems of heterosis. The whole hybrid maize program from its beginning has been based on heterosis, has exploited the phenomenon over the past forty years but as yet does not understand it. The success of the inbred-hybrid method of maize improvement is obvious to anyone familiar with the field, yet we have no definite knowledge that this is the *most* efficient method for improving all kinds of maize. In order to obtain answers to this question one might find invaluable a far more random selection of maize varieties than is represented in the United States corn belt, the place where most investigations on this problem are now concentrated. There the rigors of selection over the past half century have reduced the genetic variability of maize to a fraction of that found in many Latin American countries. In the Latin American corn collections are found varieties and races representing widely different evolutionary histories and consequently great genetic differences between races. When the evolutionary histories of these races are understood they then become ideal materials for basic studies on the heterosis problem, whether one is using the methods of modern quantitative genetics or other techniques. For example, it is already known that some races and varieties seem to contribute very little to heterosis, regardless of the kinds of crosses in which they are used. On the other hand, a few races seem to contribute a high degree of heterosis in nearly all crosses. As an example, the slender eared, high knob races of western Mexico are excellent general combiners, as are the slender eared, big butted races with very low knob numbers. Crosses between these two sorts, in spite of their close similarity in so many characters, show very high grades of heterosis. With the Latin American varieties collected, classified, and in the germ plasm bank, it should be possible to plan a truly basic investigation of the sources of heterosis in the maize varieties of the world.

GEOGRAPHY

The estimated area of Bolivia is 412,800 square miles.[1] It is the fifth largest country in South America after Brazil, Argentina, Peru and Colombia. At its greatest length it measures about 950 miles and at its greatest width about 900 miles. It is bounded by Brazil to the north and east, by Argentina and Paraguay to the south, by Peru to the north and west, and by Chile to the southwest. The country is at present entirely landlocked having lost all of its seaboard to Chile in the War of the Pacific (1879–1883).

The territory of Bolivia consists of a series of formidable contrasts between the high Andean mountain chains and plateau to the lowland tropical forests and savannas of the Amazon and La Plata basins. The extensive tropical lowlands (Oriente) make up about 70 per cent of the total area of the whole country. The eastern slopes of the Andes descend for the most part abruptly towards the lowlands as a series of steep valleys and gorges. Elevation is the most important factor in determining temperature and rainfall. Hence, almost every conceivable type of climate and scenery is found within the country, often in unusual juxtaposition as altitude changes suddenly. La Paz at about 12,000 ft. above sea level is only a short distance away from both the snow covered range at La Cumbre (15,250 ft.), and the semi-tropical mountain valleys of the Yungas (about 3,000 to 6,000 ft.).

Bolivia has been divided into six principal natural regions by Abel Penã and Lillo Escobar (46). The main characteristics of these regions are illustrated by the following table (17, 29, 44, 49).

TABLE 1. Altitude and average temperature of the six principal natural regions of Bolivia.

Region	Altitude	Average Temp.
High Andean	Above 15,000 ft.	0.C
Sub-Andean	12,000–15,000 ft.	5.C
Altiplano	7,500–12,000 ft.	8.C
Temperate Andean	4,800– 7,500 ft.	17.C
Highland Tropics	2,100– 4,800 ft.	20.C
Lowland Tropics	Below 2,100 ft.	30.C

[1] Figures for areas, altitude and climate of Bolivia vary slightly amongst different authorities (7, 23, 39, 42, 55).

The western part of Bolivia consists of the Andean mass and its many subdivisions into ridges, folds and plains. Beginning at the Knot of Vilcanota in southern Peru, two main parallel Andean chains run south through Bolivia as far as the frontier with Chile and the Argentine. The Cordillera Occidental, or western chain, which averages over 16,000 ft. in altitude, is divided into three main sections: Pacajes and Carangas in the north, the highlands of Huatacondo in Chile, and Sillicaya in the south. Some of the higher peaks reach altitudes of over 21,491 ft. (Sajama). The eastern chain, or Cordillera Real, is divided into several sections. The most northern section is about 100 miles in length from the Peruvian frontier and contains some of the highest mountains of Bolivia: Cololo (19,390 ft.), Illampu (21,522 ft.), Chachacomani (20,528 ft.), Huayana Potosí (20,407 ft.), and Illimany (21,325 ft.) which overlooks La Paz. The Cordillera of Tres Cruces follows next from which an eastern lateral chain branches toward Cochabamba to form the Cordillera of Cochabamba. South from Tres Cruces is situated the Cordillera of Los Frailes, where the Potosí mines are located, and below Los Frailes extends the Cordillera of Chichas which towards the south in the sector of Lipez divides in two arms and curves westward towards the Cordillera Occidental. Within the vast area enclosed by these two main Cordilleras is situated the high Altiplano (puña, meseta), a level tableland at about 13,000 ft. altitude. The Altiplano is approximately 500 miles long by 80 to 100 miles wide, of which about 40,000 sq. miles are situated in Bolivia. In the northern end, and partly within Peru, is situated Lake Titicaca at about 12,500 ft. above sea level. The lake is about 130 miles long by 70 miles across at its widest, and has an area of about 3,500 sq. miles including 36 islands. Some twenty-five rivers and streams flowing from the surrounding mountains feed the lake, and its only outlet is the river Desaguadero in the south. This river is about 200 miles long and flows into Lake Poopo which lies in the central part of the Bolivian Altiplano. Lake Poopo is much smaller than Titicaca (about 1,000 sq. miles), slightly lower at 12,140 ft. It is a shallow intensely salty lake with only a minor outlet.

The eastern slopes of the Cordillera Real are divided into narrow semi-tropical mountain valleys (Yungas), specially in the north where the mountain descends directly and very quickly towards the lowlands. The more open, temperate areas such as Cochabamba, Sucre and Tarija are found on the lower eastern extensions of the Cordillera Real, ("Valles Mesotermicos"). These valleys represent dissection of the plateau of varying depths. The rain, which the eastern Cordillera blocks off from the Altiplano, is deposited on the eastern valleys. High rainfall, humidity and temperature have produced the dense "mountain–jungles" in the Yungas at altitudes from 3,000 to 6,000 ft. At the lower altitudes the land slopes gradually from about 1,500–2,000 ft. down to 300 ft. or less, where the tropical lowlands proper are situated. These consist of dense tropical forests (mainly on the north), of large areas of natural pasture lands, and of open forests and savannas. The whole region is crossed by many rivers, some very large, and all flowing either into the Amazon or the La Plata systems. The watershed between the two systems is situated along a ridge of high ground which extends eastward toward the mountains of Matto Grosso in Brazil. The corridor of the Llanos de Chiquitos lies in between. To the south lie the Llanos del Sur, the Gran Chaco and the river system of the Pilcomayo and Paraguay. To the north, a complex network of rivers flows through the Llanos del Norte and the northern jungles towards the northwestern corner of Bolivia where all the rivers end up in the Madeira. The largest of these rivers are the Madre de Dios, Beni, Grande (Guapay), Mamore, San Miguel, Paragua and Guaporé (Itenez), all of which receive innumerable tributaries both from the Andes and from Matto Grosso. It is estimated that there are some 12,000 miles of navigable waters in Bolivia. This enormous system of river and lake navigation has been important since antiquity.

The range of altitude in Bolivia is from about 100 to over 6,000 meters so that the range of temperature is also extreme. At the same time, both on the puna and lowlands, radiation is very rapid so that daily variations in temperature are very marked. In the highlands this contrast also exists between sun and shade owing to the thinness of the atmosphere and intensity of sunshine. Rainfall on the Altiplano decreases progressively from north to south both in quantity and in the length of the rainy season. The occurrence of a long dry season and of dry spells during the rains, is as important in influencing vegetation and agriculture as total annual rainfall. Furthermore, there is much variability in the distribution of local rainfall both in the mountains and tropics. In general the rainy season lasts from December to March; the dry from April to November.

The Eastern Cordillera of Bolivia is divided at about the latitude of La Paz into two distinct sections to the north and south. The northern narrow section is a region of steep declivities, spurs and swift rivers, while the southern and wider section consists of table lands, large valleys and graded rivers. In the north, rain falls almost all the year round and the valleys are always humid, being covered for part of every day by masses of clouds. Rain is lighter in the south and hot humid valleys such as those of the northern Yungas are rare. The climate of these southern valleys is warm, dry and very pleasant for human habitation all the year round.

The following figures illustrate some of the principal climatic features of the country (17, 46, 66).

	Altitude (ft.)	Mean Annual Temp.* (C.)	Mean Annual Rainfall * (mm)
Potosí	13,255	6°	608.5
Oruro	12,160	8°	580.0
La Paz	12,130	9.8°	622.4
Sucre	9,460	12.0°	650.3
Cochabamba	8,392	18.0°	506.5
Tarija	6,250	17.5°	406.0
Santa Cruz	1,476	15.3°	1,359.0
Cobija	853	27.0°	1,770.0
Riberalta	564	27.5°	1,579.0

* All figures approximate.

NATURAL VEGETATION AND AGRICULTURE

The most important agricultural regions of Bolivia are situated on the Altiplano and in the Temperate and Tropical Highland Valleys. The Andean region is too cold for agriculture, and even the Altiplano is generally too cold for maize. At the other extreme, the hot tropical lowlands are still largely undeveloped for agriculture though several crops, including maize are grown, and the more accessible and promising regions, such as Santa Cruz, are now in process of agricultural development (*66*). Cárdenas (*10, 11*) has divided Bolivia into the following geobotanical zones: Altiplano, Vertientes Orientales de los Andes, Valles Mesotérmicos, Sabanas Orientales, Pampas de Mojos, Hylea and Chaco.

THE ALTIPLANO

The immense level high plateau of Bolivia was the center of Tiahuanaco culture, and formed the Kollasuyo region of the Inca Empire. Despite the cold, arid climate, poor, rather alkaline soils and harsh aspect of nature, this region has been for centuries the most densely populated part of the country. Mining is the most important activity at present. Some authorities have advanced the hypothesis that in prehistoric times the Altiplano had a milder climate and a greater rainfall than now, while others believe that Lake Titicaca and the other Altiplano lakes are remnants of a large inland sea which once covered the whole plateau.

Large areas of the Altiplano are covered with ichu (*Stipa pungens*), a coarse plant eaten only by llamas and used mainly for thatching native huts. Fuel is provided by several hardy shrubs, specially yareta (*Azorella geabre*) and tola (*Lepidophyllum quadrangulare*). There is an almost complete absence of trees. The flowering shrub Khantuta whose crimson flower is the national emblem of Bolivia, is common in and around villages. Cacti, kishuara and other plants grow in small patches in the more protected places. Around Lake Titicaca, tule and totora (*Scirpus totora*) grows in abundance and is used for building the light fishing boats (balsas) characteristic of the lake.

The most important crop is the potato, which is the staple food of the highland native population. Other important crops are quinoa (*Chenopodium quinoa*), barley, canhui (*Atriplex canahui*), and other edible tubers of the Altiplano such as oca (*Oxalis tuberosa*). Maize is grown to some extent, mainly in the sheltered and warmer places near Lake Titicaca. Both the more moderate climate and fertile soils of the lake region make it into an area of relatively intense agriculture. The livestock consists mainly of the typical Andean llamas, alpacas and vicuñas.

The largest city of Bolivia, La Paz, is situated a short distance away from Lake Titicaca in a large depression in the plateau. The lake once drained into the Amazon basin through this gorge in which the La Paz river now flows. The lower altitude and sheltered situation of the city and valley makes the climate and vegetation of La Paz different from that of the Altiplano proper. The famous ruins of the pre-Inca city of Tihuancao as well as many Inca ruins are situated near La Paz a short distance away from Lake Titicaca. The whole of the Altiplano region in both Peru and Bolivia, but specially near Lake Titicaca, is rich in indigenous highland traditions and possesses immense archeological and historical interest.

THE HIGHLAND VALLEYS

The Temperate Highland Valleys are strictly speaking part of the Bolivian plateau and are situated principally in the south, in the Departments of Cochabamba, Sucre and Tarija. The Tropical Highland Valleys, on the other hand, are situated on the "Ceja de Montaña", the slopes leading down directly to the tropical rain forests (Montaña) in the lowlands. They consist principally of the Yungas of the Departments of La Paz and Cochabamba, and the valleys of Luribay, Cinti, Mizque, Muyripampa, Entre Ríos, Turuchipa and others. The Yungas, with a semitropical humid climate (rainfall at Coroico, 800 mm) and constant fogs are heavily wooded and possess a varied forest vegetation. The character of this vegetation is to some extent dependent on situation and soils, but it includes cedar, mahogany, walnut, many kinds of palms, ceiba and several medicinal trees such as cinchona, the source of the quinine bark. There is an abundance of epiphytic ferns, lichens and mosses. Sauer (55) divides the Yungas into three zones: "The cabecera del valle, above 8,528 ft. (2,600 m); between 8,500 and 5,500 ft. (2,000 and 1,700 m) the valle or medio yunga; below 5,500 ft. (1,700 m) the yunga, devoted to warm land crops. Potatoes are grown in the higher elevations, maize throughout but most successfully and of greatest variety at the intermediate heights." Cárdenas (10, 11) recognizes one more zone situated at 10,200 ft. (3,400 m) which he calls "Ceja de Monte," with a rainfall of over 2,000 mm. The vegetation of this zone is characterized by the following genera: Ericaceae, Myrtaceae, *Podocarpus unbigena, Oreopanas čartocarpoides, Clusia pseudomangle, Tra-*

poeolum kunzeanum, Melastomaceae, Fuchsia, etc. Access to the Yungas and penetration into them is very difficult. Stream courses and valleys are the easiest and it is on these that the population of the area is concentrated.

The main agricultural activity of the inhabitants of the Yungas is the production of coca (*Erythroxylon coca*), the leaves of which are consumed in large quantities by the Indian population of the highlands. The crops of the region consist mainly of sweet potato, sweet manioc, sugar cane, tobacco, coffee, cocas, maize, and a variety of semi-tropical fruits.

The temperate valleys with their year round spring-like climate produce all the products of temperate lands and many of the fruits of the Tropical lowlands. The broad level valley of Cochabamba has been called the "granary of Bolivia." Maize is one of the most important crops. At Tarija, which is lower than Cochabamba, tobacco is grown. Rainfall in these valleys is not always adequate, and the water supply must be supplemented with irrigation. The natural vegetation is characterized by algarrobo (*Prosopio juliflora*) molle (*Schinus molle*), tipa (*Tipuana speciosa*), pino (*Podocarpus parlatorei*), chirimolle (*Fogara coco*), etc., etc.

THE TROPICAL LOWLANDS (ORIENTE)

The Oriente consists of dense tropical rain forest (Montaña, salva, matorral), open forest and savanna (llanos) and areas of open natural pasture. Rivers form the most important feature and the chief means of communication. During the period of the rains vast areas are flooded, while in the summer months drought conditions occur. A large lake once occupied the center of the Beni region. The river waters were trapped by a granite barrier in the north until erosive action broke through it at the present channel on the Maderia. The present swamps between the rivers Mamoré and Beni, and the lakes Rogoaguado and Rogagua are remnants of this vast ancient lake. Navigation is still obstructed by the rapids (cachuelas) as the rivers flow through the northern barrier.

The whole region is very flat and, unlike much of the Amazon basin, largely alluvial. The southern region includes the savanna, open scrub and woodland of the Bolivian Chaco. The tropical forest lies mainly in the north (most of the Department of Pando,

and along the rivers Beni, Orton and Madre de Dios), in an area
extending from Santa Cruz to the Beni, and along the rivers
Guaporé and Paraguay. The larger areas of tropical savanna are
situated in the Santa Cruz region and eastwards and westwards
from it towards the Brazilian frontier and the Mojos and Beni
plains. Part of the northern Provinces of Velasco and Ñuflo de
Chavez are also included. The palm totai (*Acronia totai*) is characteristic of the savanna. The Mojos plains include mainly the
large area in the Provinces of Yacuma, Mojos and part of Itenez
which is subject to extensive annual flooding. The whole region is
covered with high grass dotted with many "islands" of forests.

MAIZE GROWING REGIONS

Maize and potatoes are the two most important crops grown in
Bolivia. Maize area and production in 1950 (the data of the last
agricultural census), by Departments was as follows (*18*):

TABLE 2. Area and Production of Maize in Bolivia

(Excluding green corn—choclo)

Departments	Area (Ha.)	Production (Kilos)
Chuquisaca	31,003.31	30,622.767
Cochabamba	21,953.20	25,130.082
Santa Cruz	19,176.82	30,960.683
Potosí	18,524.89	16,133.409
Tarija	13,425.91	12,939.068
La Paz	9,381.21	9,785.458
Beni	1,899.51	3,060.866
Pando	684.92	1,064.600
Oruro	2.33	4.143
Totals	116,052.10	129,701.086

The most important maize growing areas in each Department
can be loosely linked together into a crescent extending from
immediately north of Lake Titicaca to the Department of Cochabamba, part of western Santa Cruz and south through Sucre and
Potosí to the border with the Argentina in the western part of the
Department of Tarija. The following are the most important
centers accounting for over half of the total area.

Within this "maize belt," the most isolated and least important
part is that situated in the north western part of the Department
of La Paz. This area is separated from the Cochabamba region by

the Altiplano and by the Yungas. Maize production in the northern Yungas is very small (about 600 ha.). The adjacent north
western provinces of Murillo, Muñecas and Larecaja have a maize
area of about 5,000 ha. The Province of Inquisivi on the eastern

TABLE 3. Principal Maize Growing Areas by Provinces

Department	Province	Area (Ha.)
La Paz	Muñecas	2,569
Cochabamba	Ayopaya	3,489
	Quillacollo	2,740
	Mizque	2,582
	Campero	2,285
		11,096
Potosí	Charcas	5,082
	Chayanta	3,339
	S. Chichas	2,504
		10,925
Santa Cruz	Vallegrande	5,063
	Florida	2,230
	Cordillera	4,487
		11,780
Chuquisaca	Zudañez	2,175
	Tomina	5,211
	Azurduy	2,277
	Nor Cinti	5,937
	Azero	3,763
	Calvo	6,801
		26,164
Tarija	Cercado	3,165
	O'Connor	2,254
	Arce	3,211
		8,630
Total		71,164

slopes of the Andes border on the Cochabamba Province of
Ayopaya is part of this latter region. The heart of the Bolivian
maize growing region is situated in the Temperate Highland
Valley south of the Cordillera of Cochabamba, and east of the
Cordillera Real. In the central part the drainage runs southwards
into the Grande Guapay River, and in the southern part into the

Pilcomayo and Bermejo. The Grande river at first runs eastwards
and then curves northwards east of Santa Cruz to flow towards the
Mamore system. Several rivers also flow towards the Mamore
from the northern slopes of the Cordillera of Cochabamba, of
which the more important are the Chapare, Ichilo and Yapacone.
Small quantities of maize are also grown on these areas, specially
at Chapare and Carrasco. Most of the maize produced in the lowlands of the Departments of Beni and Pando is grown in isolated
patches, mainly along the river valleys near population centers.

MAIZE AND THE INDIGENOUS PEOPLES OF BOLIVIA

The variety and the ebb and flow of peoples on the South
American continent in the distant as well as in the recent past is
well represented in Bolivia. The country has been called a
"museum of peoples" (36). The principal groups of Indians in
Bolivia at the present time are the Aymara and Quechua of the
highlands; the Chiriguano (Tupi-Guaraní) of southern Bolivia; the
many tribes of the Yungas and eastern slopes belonging to different linguistic families (Arawakan, Takanen, Panoan), and also
to isolated linguistic groups such as the Leco; and the tribes of the
lowlands proper of which the Mojos—Chiquitos area is the largest.
"No other area in South America," according to Steward (62) "has
greater linguistic diversity." At the present time most of these
peoples of Bolivia are agriculturalists and cultivate maize and
other crops, and the classification of some primitive groups as
"marginal non-agriculturalists" (60) has been seriously questioned
by Hohenthal (21).

The archeological evidence for the Central Andean region in
what is now Peru and Bolivia begins with cultures already fully
developed. This evidence goes back, for the most part, to about
the beginning of the Christian era by which time both the highland region and the Peruvian coastal region had already developed complicated agricultural techniques; pottery, weaving, building, many other crafts, and an advanced political organization.
The highlands, therefore, have been occupied for a long period
by a sedentary Indian population engaged in agriculture, pastoral
pursuits, and advanced activities such as metallurgy. But, although archeological material for earlier periods is still insufficient,

it is probable that the nomadic hunters of Paloeo-American period such as the Patagonia types (4, 5) may have once lived in the central highlands. But evidence of agricultural beginnings does not exist. The earliest archeological evidence of agriculture in South America is that found by Bird in his excavation of Huaca Prieta on the coastal area of Peru, dated between 2,370 and 2,578 B.C. approximately (3, 6). Maize is missing from the earlier levels and appears only with Guañape-Cupisnique culture (about 1,250–500 B.C.).

Some authors believe that the Aymara peoples of the highlands are of great antiquity (37, 40, 47, 48). The absence of evidence of an earlier race than the Aymara on the Bolivian highlands has been questioned by authors who think that the Urus and Chipayas are remnants of peoples who immigrated to the highlands in the remote past (64). They probably came from the Amazon basin region and extended their influence to the Pacific coast. A sub-stratum of Amazonian traits appears to be common to the Andean cultures. This is sufficiently evident in the Chavin culture (1,200-400 B.C.), and roughly parallel to Cupisnique of Peru to have led Tello (63) to suggest that the early Andean peoples came from the tropical lowlands. A later cultural influence in the reverse direction is also evident in archeological material from the lowlands. The influence of Tiahuanaco and Inca is, for instance, evident in the Mojos region of Bolivia, a county in which Andean "influence extended farther east than in Peru and Ecuador." (Steward, v. 43, p. 510. 62). Nevertheless, the geographical barrier of the Andes—jungle boundary has always remained a cultural barrier as well, so that extensive direct influence and blending did not occur even in Inca times. The Chiriguano of southern Bolivia, an isolated Guarani group, who crossed the Chaco in the 15th century to raid for gold in Inca territory, and to attack the Chané tribes, settled in the conquered area and had extensive contacts with the Incas, but remained a distinct group. At the same time, they acted as intermediates between the Andes and the Chaco: "even today the Tapieté hire themselves to the Chiriguano in return for supplies of maize" (34). On the whole, as pointed out by Tello (63), the people of the fertile Andean valleys (in which populations were concentrated, e.g. Cuzco and Lake Titicaca), were able to exchange products with the inhabitants of both jungle and altiplano.

The story of migration of peoples on the American continent in ancient times has not been even approximately unravelled yet, least of all for the eastern lowlands of South America. Existing primitive semi-nomadic groups such as the Sirionos of Bolivia (54) or the Ge of Brazil, may possibly represent remnants of the earliest people to occupy these regions of the continent. On the other hand, there is some evidence that agricultural peoples may have pre-dated them. Nordenskiöld (36, 54) for instance, discovered in the area between Trinidad and Asución, south of Casarobe, now inhabited by the Sirione, mounds of earth built up so as to obtain dry sites for dwellings in the wet season. Excavations showed that the region must have been inhabited in the past by "Indians possessing a well developed art in ceramics, and who were agriculturalists with maize as an important cultivated plant" (54). These Indians boiled their maize, and unlike the other Indian groups of the lowlands, used grooved earthenware grinding slab and grooved mullers instead of the usual wooden mortar.

The migration of peoples from the north and specially the Caribbean area through the lowlands to what is now Peru, Brazil and Bolivia, is well established (37, 50, 57, 59). They moved along the rivers for long distances until they reached the foothills of the Andes. One of the most extensive of these migrations was that of the Arawaks, of which there are several groups in Bolivia extending across the central Bolivian lowlands (Beni) from the Apolista group of the Yungas and the Mojo and Bauré of the Llanos del Norte, to the Paikoneka, Saraveka and Paressi tribes of the east and Brazilian border (31, 33, 57, 59). The southern Chané, whose territory was overrun by the Guarani in historic times, are also Arawak. The Takana groups of north Bolivia and some isolated groups (Panoan of southern Peru and north Bolivia), separate the Bolivian Arawaks from the northern block of Arawak which extend from the Peruvian lowlands of the Ucayali eastwards to Brazil (Campa, Masco, Maniteri, Piro, Canameri and Ipurina). The linguistic affinities of the highland Urus and Chipayas of Granges, and Lake Titicaca Pukina, are all Arawakan (57, 59).

The Arawaks are people possessing a settled agriculture based largely on the cultivation of maize. The importance of maize to them has been described by Radin (50): "Never in their far flung travels did they give it up. Much of what was specifically theirs they had at times perforce to surrender. Even so vital a factor in their culture as the boat was lost in the more remote corners of this new world, and much of their language itself, but never maize. This always remains the specific trait that informs us that we are still in the area of Arawak culture with all the other outlines of their ancient island tradition.

However, it is well established that the Chiquitos (meaning "the small one") were good agriculturalists and cultivated maize. To the east of the Chiquitos and extending into Brazil, the area of Bororo speaking tribes begins, but extremely few individuals remain in Bolivia. The Guaporé River in this region "is a frontier rather than a link. The Mojo-Chiquito culture area extends from the left bank towards the Andes: the heterogenous tribes on the right bank have a definitely Amazonian culture" (25).

Maize is also important amongst the more southern Chiriguano who adopted the customs of the agricultural Chané, whose territory they occupied. The Chiriguano in this respect, differ from the typical Guarani peoples of their homeland in the Chaco, who rely on hunting and fishing to a greater extent. The Chaco can be considered as a transitional region between the tropical Llanos of the north and the Argentinian Pampas to the south. Nordenskiöld (36) considered that the Chaco peoples have been greatly influenced by contact with Andean people in the west. Métraux (34) has listed additional links with the Andes, and concludes that "knowledge of agriculture probably came from the Andean region." It is likely that the Arawakan agricultural Chané played an important role in spreading Andean culture to the east, situated as they were between the Chaco and the Andes. North of the Chiriguano territory, roughly between Santa Cruz and Cochabamba, are situated the Yurakare and the related and more northern Chimane and Mosetene. These peoples mainly occupy the tropical forest dwellers subsisting by a combination of farming, fishing and hunting. The Leco is a small group on the Huanay river area who specialize in navigation of the Beni river, and

whose chief staple foods are maize and bananas. North of the
Leco, where the city of Apolo is situated is another small, isolated
group, the Apolista (or Lapacu), which has Arawak linguistic affinities. It consists of a few individuals in a Quechua speaking
population.

The present limit between the Quechua and Aymara speaking
populations of the highlands of Bolivia is situated northeast of
Lake Titicaca at Cojota, and northwest of the Lake of Puno in
Peru. The exact relationships between the two peoples is a
matter of controversy, as is the whole story of the Tiahuanaco
civilization itself. The end of this civilization (traces of which
have been found from coastal Peru to the Argentine) perhaps came
in a sudden catastrophe which left the great Tiahuanaco center
near Lake Titicaca unfinished, and led to chaos and disorder.
Out of this, the Quechuas and the Incas arose to create the Inca
civilization. There is no certainty regarding the duration of the
Inca empire. The Spanish chronicles vary widely in their estimates from 300 to 1,000 years (27, 28, 41). But the main period of
Inca development, consolidation and expansion is almost certainly
to have occurred from the 12th century A.D. onwards.

The history of maize in America, as recorded by the Spanish
chroniclers, has been recently reviewed by Mesa Bernal (30).
Similarly, Latchman (22) and Parodi (45) have written on maize in
South America in pre-Colombian times. In all cases it is made
abundantly clear that maize, in what is now Bolivia, was an extremely important crop. The main types cultivated by the Indians
at the time of the conquest in the general area of the Bolivian
highlands were as follows (22):

Type	Quechua Name	Aymara Name
Hard, small kernel	murucho	morochi
Black or purple	kullisara	collitonco
Yellow	huilcaparu	churi
White	paracaysara	missatonco

Many other types (Kullikueei, pucatonco, etc.) and names of types
are mentioned by the chroniclers but it is often difficult to distinguish the territory where they were grown.

In general, the Spanish chroniclers describe two main distinct
types: Morocho and Capia. The first type (murucho, morochi in

Quechua and Aymara; pataschka in Atacoma; muhua in Araucano) was a small to medium hard type, rounded kernel, and of a red-purple color, which gave a flour of a very high quality. This type was essentially a popcorn ("confite"). Acosta (*1*) described it as "chico y sequillo." [1] The maize type described by Garcilaso de la Vega (*19, 20*) as Capia (ckappa) was, on the contrary "tierno y de mucho regalo" [2] and, according to Acosta (*1*), "grueso y sustancioso" [3] and was undoubtedly a soft large kerneled flour type of which there were many varieties. Acosta distinguished two of these: "redondo y grueso," but most of these varieties were distinguished by the name of the predominant color of the kernels. In addition, there are some records also of the eastern lowland maize types (micha in Peru; missa in Bolivia; anona and amapo in Venezuela) which was characterized as being extremely early ("maiz cuarenteno"). This maize is represented by types still grown in Bolivia, specially by the Mojos (the "maize was ready for harvest in two months") (*22, 59*).

Amongst the most complete description of maize and its uses is that given by Cobo (*14*): "Crece tan en breve en algunas partes, que dentro de tres o cuatro meses, y aun a veces dentro de dos, si siembra, coge y encierra. Son muchas las diferencias que hay de maiz; porque, primeramente se halla de todos colores: blanco, negro y amarillo, morado, colorado claro y oscuro y mezclado de varios colores. Diferenciose, demos desto, en el tamano de los granos; los mayores que se hayan son poco menos que habas. Hay un maíz muy tierno, de harina muy blanca y suave, y otro muy duro que los indios llaman murucho, y los españoles, morocho, que ordinariamente couren las cabalgaduras; y a todas estas diferencias tienen puesto los indios nombres propios." [4]

[1] Historia Natural y Moral de Indias, Chapter 16, Book 4: "Del Pan de Indios y del Maíz." Trans: "small and rather dry."

[2] Comentarios Reales, Chapter 9, Book 8. Trans: soft and/or rich taste."

[3] As above. Trans: "broad and nourishing."

[4] Free translation: "Maize grows so rapidly in some parts, that in three to four months, and even, sometimes in two, it is sown, harvested and stored. There are many differences in maize; firstly, it is of every colour: white, black and yellow, purple, light and dark and mixtures of various colours. In addition there are differences in the size of the kernel; the largest that are found are like beans. There is a very tender maize, with a white and soft flour and another one that is very hard and that the Indians call murucho, and the Spaniards morocho, which is the type ordinarily fed to horses; and for all these differences the Indians have a specific name."

MAIZE CULTIVATION AND USES

The pre-Conquest indigenous pattern of agriculture based upon the cultivation of maize and potatoes, and in the absence of oxen, on the hoe and spade, still occurs in the highlands of Peru and Bolivia. Barley, wheat and other crops have been introduced, and also sheep, and, in some areas, cattle and forage crops. The introduced plants and animals are becoming increasingly important, but so long as maize continues to be a major article for direct human consumption in an indigenous subsistence economy, it will not lose its pre-eminence as the staple cereal of Bolivia. The trend towards more uniformity has probably already reduced the number of distinct types of maize, and has influenced cultivation methods.

Maize is cultivated in Bolivia mainly by small farmers. The variability of terrain and climate, and the multiple uses of the crop, makes the choice of varieties a most important factor in cultivation. Length of growing period is the first main consideration, and this is closely associated with the availability of supplementary irrigation. Where both irrigation and very early varieties are available, two crops may be obtained in a year. At the same time, a late variety (270 days) will give a poor yield in areas where the rainy season is too short to sustain growth. Under entirely rain fed conditions, the date of planting, in relation to local seasonal variation in rainfall, may make all the difference between a good yield in any one year. Normal planting dates are October to December, and the harvest is from about April to July. Where irrigation is available late varieties can be planted as early as August or September.

The importance of irrigation in the cultivation of Andean maize, both in antiquity and at the present time, cannot be over-emphasized. A great part of the variability of the maize of Peru and Bolivia is due to selection for the greater range or adaptability made possible by irrigation. Highland maize, as a whole, varies in growing period from about 150 to 270 days. The choice of variety is thus a complex matter in which account has to be taken of altitude and temperatures, length of rainfall period, soil fertility and uses. Where irrigation is available, however, the possibilities in any given region are greatly increased. It has been suggested

(50, 58) that the advanced irrigation techniques of the Indians were the results of a pressing need to irrigate maize, for, in general, potatoes and quinoa were cultivated on non-irrigated land.

The vast scale and skill of the irrigation works of the Quechuas and Aymaras has been often described and is well known. These works existed even on the high Altiplano itself, using the waters of the Desaguadero (Chacamarcha) river (58). The first task of the Incas upon conquering new territories was always to build irrigation works for the specific purpose of planting maize. In the warmer valleys terracing and irrigation occurred together. Regions of favourable climate for maize and other crops in the Andean highlands are generally in narrow valleys where the amount of cultivable land in the valley bottom is limited. Terraces filled with choice soil, irrigated and intensely fertilized were the principal solutions to this problem, for this made possible the cultivation of high yielding maize even under climatic conditions imposing a very long growing period together with a short rainfall season. The highest yielding varieties of the whole Andean region of Peru and Bolivia are still the rather late "Cuzco types" of soft flour maize. The Cuzco and Urubamba valleys of Peru were the focus of agricultural development during the Inca period, specially in irrigation, terracing and maize selection. Cuzco maize types are widespread in Bolivia, and while this is a result of cultural influence, it is also due to the higher yielding qualities of the maize, itself, when grown under irrigation. Even at the present time some Bolivian farmers in irrigated areas on or near the Altiplano (mainly in the La Paz and northern valleys) bring "new maize seed" direct from Cuzco whenever possible. The problem in the maize growing areas of Bolivia situated in the temperate highland valleys is to combine early maturity with high yields. The early maturing types of the Altiplano give low yields. The Uchuquilla maize of Cochabamba is perhaps the nearest approximation to this standard. It is a semi-hard type with a growing period of about 150 days, used mainly for flour.

In the lowland regions of Bolivia maize cultivation, like agriculture in general, is at a very primitive level. Small patches of cultivated land occur on forest clearings near rivers and on dry river beds. There is the minimum of care and cultivation and yields are very poor. Irrigation is nonexistent. The maize grown has a very short growing season, and much of it is eaten as green corn. Where Caribbean flint types have been introduced in recent years and good cultivation practices are followed, excellent crops are obtained.

The close relationship between uses of maize, its cultivation, and the spread of Andean types from the Lake Titicaca—Cuzco regions to other parts of the highlands, is well illustrated by Inca practices associated with religious reverence for Lake Titicaca and its islands. Everything that came from this area had a special significance and was the object of worship, including maize. Sebastian Llorente, as stated by Latchman (22), describes how the maize of Lake Titicaca was distributed and sown in all the other regions of the Inca empire "como prendas de inestimable valor; y el que alcanzaba la rara dicha de poseer algunos granos, creía firmemente que echados en su pirhua o sembrador en su campo traerían sobre su maíz los benficios de lo alto." [1] For the Indian the magical and religious significance of maize was profound since it was the expression of the fertility of the land which linked man and his gods. Hence, the growing and care of special types of maize was a means of religious intercession. But the main reason for this adoration of maize and for its religious significance arose undoubtedly from the unique value of the plant to the Indian. It was not only a food and drink, but also had multiple other uses in medicine, in the provision of shelter ("pirka"), as forage for animals, as fuel (the "marlo" or cob), in divination, in games, in personal adornment, as a dye, as vinegar from chicha—which also served as an acid for working metal—,as a wrapping material for other foods, and in many other ways. In this sense, the civilization of the Andes was a "maize culture." Maize was "un proteo que se transformaba en todo y acompanaba al hombre desde el nacimiento hasta la tumba" (43). [2]

Some of these uses persist to this day in Bolivia, specially the different ways of preparing the maize kernel for food for human

[1] As being of the highest value whoever had the unusual luck of obtaining a few grains, firmly believed that if those were sown in his cornfields, that they would bring benefits from heaven.

[2] Something which transformed itself into anything and which accompanied man from the crib to the tomb.

consumption. Amongst the most important of these are "maiz tostado" or "cancha (parched or roasted maize), "choclo" (green corn), "mote" (boiled maize), "chicha" (maize beer), and maize flour, which is used in a variety of ways. But leavening, which was unknown by the Incas, is not used. To some extent different varieties of maize are still used for different purposes, but most varieties have multiple uses, of which flour and chicha are the most important. Typical of this is the variety Huilcaparu which is widely grown in the Andean Valleys of Bolivia. The preparation of maize by boiling followed by grinding into a dough as in Mexico is not practiced in Bolivia or Peru. Grinding is always done on the dry maize to produce a dry flour or meal. A partly ground or rough ground meal (maiz "triturado") is sometimes made in Bolivia for the preparation of a special porridge ("mazamorra") called Tojorí. When the maize is fully ground a similar porridge is made called Api. In both cases sugar and spices may be added. Varieties Checchi and Chuspillu are preferred for Tojorí, and Kulli for Api. For "mazamorra morada," the purple Kulli is used. Kulli is an early variety, and it is also used for chicha. But Chuspillu, which is later, and a "sweet" maize, produces a better quality and highly alcoholic chicha (huiñapu).

Chicha has been the chief intoxicating drink of the peoples of both tropical and highland Bolivia, as of most of the American continent, from the earliest times to the present day. The word is used for intoxicating beverages made from many different plants (algarroba, oca, quinoa, sugar cane, mainhot, and several fruits), but maize chicha is the most important. There are many different ways of making chicha which vary both from region to region and within a given region (13). But in all cases the best chicha is considered to be that made from soft types of maize. In addition, the fermenting substance for the best chicha is generally saliva. In this case the maize is chewed almost exclusively by women.

Mote or boiled maize is of two kinds. In both cases the maize is first boiled with ashes (preferably of molle) and lime, to remove the pericarp. For the making of tamales—a Mexican introduction —the kernels are ground into a masa or dough. The usual practice in Bolivia and Peru, however, is to dry the kernels in the sun to produce mote seco (dry mote) or chochoca. Mote is a soft maize

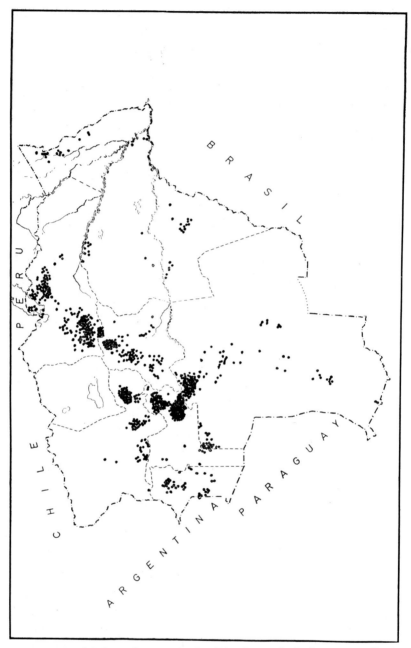

Fɪɢ. 1. Map of Bolivia showing the localities from which the maize collections
were made.

Although the total number of knobs characterizing a particular race of maize has considerable value in classification, a much more critical use of knob data is that having to do with the position, size and shape of specific knobs of specific chromosomes. This kind of analysis is made possible by the fact that knobs occur at certain points and only at certain points on the chromosome. Additionally, knobs occupying a particular position on the chromosome vary both in size and shape and these characteristics are also of importance when using knob data as an indicator of relationships in maize. For example one might find that for a given geographical area all the maize is characterized by three knobs. If it is not known on which chromosomes these three knobs are found, the only conclusion one can draw from such data is that the maize of the area is characterized by a low number of knobs. Whereas, if information on knob position, size and shape is available, one can then determine the exact knob consitution of any particular race or plant of maize and can draw valid conclusions as to cytological relationship, even in situations where total number of knobs may not differ.

There has been much discussion in the literature relative to the origin of knobs in maize, as to whether the presence of a large number of knobs, for example, indicates admixture with teosinte or *Tripsacum* and conversely, whether the absence of knobs or presence of a few knobs only suggest a lack of close relationship to these two related genera. There is abundant evidence, it seems to us, that reciprocal introgression between Z. *mays* and teosinte has occurred over relatively long periods of time in regions where the two taxa inhabit common environments and the process is undoubtedly continuing even today. As a result, much modern maize contains varying proportions of teosinte, and vice versa. It may be, therefore, that at least some of the chromosome knobs now carried by maize were introduced via the hybridization route with teosinte. However, since we know so little about knob origins, it seems premature to consider the direction of migration of knobs at this time. It could be from one genus to another or there may have been mutual exchange of knobs between the two genera. If the theory of Mangelsdorf and Reeves (26) postulating a hybrid origin for teosinte resulting from a cross of *Zea* and

Tripsacum, is finally proven, it then naturally follows that some chromosome knobs of maize could be ultimately derived from *Tripsacum.* Since the cytological data from the Bolivian races seems to shed little light on this problem, and since it is now known that different species of *Tripsacum* have widely different knob numbers and positions we prefer in this discussion to postpone questions of knob origin and to use the knob information reported here only as another character for determining possible relationships.

The knob counts and positions contained herein were obtained by Dr. Barbara McClintock; it is through her kind permission that we are reporting them. These data should be considered as of preliminary nature since (1) they include only eighteen of the thirty-two races of Bolivian maize described in this study; (2) due to the limited time at her disposal, Dr. McClintock was able to sample relatively few plants within any given race studied; and (3) before the final significance of these results become apparent it will be necessary to obtain additional knob numbers and positions for the races of maize from other countries of South America, Central America and Mexico.

Although limited, the information we have on knobs of the Bolivian races presents an amazingly consistent picture from the standpoint of geographical distribution, and also gives strong support to the validity of the classification of these corns made prior to the availability of any cytological facts. As will be noted in Table 4 each of the highland races studied have almost identical knob constitution with the exception of the race *Pisankalla.* The latter is a popcorn and is quite distinct morphologically from the other high altitude races. It resembles some lowland popcorns much more closely than it does such highland popcorns as Confite Puneño.

The races *Confite Puneño, Altiplano, Kulli, Huilcaparu, Checchi, Paru, Chuspillu, Uchuquilla, Karapampa* and *Niñuelo* are all from elevations of 1800 to 3800 meters. They are each highland Andean corns, and, in so far as their chromosome knob constitution is concerned, they represent an extremely homogeneous group. For example, every plant examined (56 in all) carried a medium to small knob in the long arm of each chromosome 7.

The only other knob present in any of these races is a very small one at the lower position on the long arm of chromosome 6. Among the 56 plants examined, 44 contained this knob, and in the remaining 12, chromosome 6 was knobless. In each of these Andean races all other chromosomes were without knobs. It is, therefore, clear from these data that a definite and consistent knob pattern is present in the high altitude races of Bolivia. In the present discussion we are following Dr. McClintock in referring to this pattern as "Andean." As will be shown later and in subsequent papers this pattern is found not only in Bolivia but in other parts of highland South America as well.

Bolivian races from the lowlands and from intermediate altitudes have knob numbers, positions, sizes and shapes quite distinct from those of the highlands. Disregarding the race *Pisankalla* for the moment, as one moves from high altitudes to lower elevations, the numbers of knobs encountered tend to increase and knob patterns as well as degrees of homozygosity and heterozygosity of knob constitutions tend to change. The decrease in numbers, however, is not always in direct proportion to altitude (Table 5). *Coroico* and *Enano*, for example, are found at elevations of 120 to approximately 200 meters. Despite the fact that they are lowland corns they both have knob patterns very similar to that typifying the Andean races. Among four examined plants of one collection of *Enano*, all carried the same medium-small knob in the long arm of each chromosome 7 that characterizes the Andean races of maize. In addition, a smaller knob at the lower position in the long arm of each chromosome 6 was present in these plants. In three of the four plants, no other knobs were present, but in the fourth, a large knob was present in the long arm of one of the two chromosomes 4. *Coroico*, from the same area, also carries a medium-small knob in the long arm of chromosome 7 and a very small knob in chromosome 6 typical of the Andean type. In addition to these knobs one of two examined plants derived from a small collection had knobs on chromosomes 2 and 4 and one of two examined plants of another collection carried a small knob in one of its two chromosomes 5. It would seem then, on the basis of knob data, that both *Coroico* and *Enano* are essentially "Andean" in their knob compositions.

The race *Pisankalla,* although occurring in the highlands (1900–2500 meters), does not possess the typical Andean knob pattern. This is not surprising when one compares *Pisankalla* with the other highland races from the same region. The former is a popcorn whose ears and plants are very unlike those of other races from the same areas. It varies in the form of the plant and the ear within collections and from collection to collection. The knob constitution of chromosome 6 and 7 of *Pisankalla* does not differ greatly from that of the other highland races, but in addition to chromosome 6 and 7, knobs were found on chromosomes 1, 2, 4, 5, 8 and 9 (Table 5). Despite the occurrence of considerable variation between collections, there is a fair degree of consistency in knob constitutions in the various plants and collections of plants. For example, the knob in chromosome 7 is in the small arm. It is either small or medium-small or heterozygous small, medium small. The knob in chromosome 6 is always very small when present and at the lower position in the long arm. The knob in the long arm of chromosome 8, when present, is always large and at the upper position. The knob in chromosome 4 is always large and the knob in chromosome 5 is always medium in size, when present.

The knob data suggest that *Pisankalla* may result from crosses between races with very different knob constitutions. These knobs are segregating among individuals of the populations from which the collections were made. Therefore, there is considerable degree of heterozygosity exhibited with respect to a particular knob. On the basis of knob data one might assume that one parent of *Pisankalla* was probably an Andean race. The identification of other putative parent or parents must await the results of study of additional races from the area in which *Pisankalla* is grown.

Of the four remaining races for which we have knob determinations, one of these, *Pojoso chico,* carries the typical pattern of the Andean type plus knobs from unknown sources on chromosomes 2, 4 and 9. This, it will be recalled, is similar to the knob situation in the closely related race *Coroico.* The race *Perola* possesses a knob pattern which can be classified as "Venezuelan" plus "Chilean" while *Pororo* and *Cholito* appear to be "Chilean" plus "Venezuelan." The terms "Chilean" and "Venezuelan" are here used to designate what has been found to be the most frequently occurring knob patterns among the relatively few collections examined from those countries.

B TYPE CHROMOSOMES

Among Bolivian corns B type chromosomes are common in the highland races. Of the eleven races characterized by the Andean knob pattern, B types were found to occur in ten. The maximum number of B's observed in any one plant was 6 in one collection of the race *Checchi.* Among the races from lowland and intermediate elevations B types were present only in two collections. However, since the number of lowland races studied were relatively few, a comparison of the frequency of B types between these two groups is hardly justified. We have no way of knowing whether a study of more lowland races would have altered this picture.

In summary, the cytological information available shows very clearly the presence of a distinct chromosome knob pattern in the highland races. This pattern has been designated "Andean" and with the exception of one popcorn it fits all the high altitude races studied. Furthermore, an examination of races from other South American countries shows this same Andean pattern to be present in the highland races of Chile and Ecuador, and it will undoubtedly be found in Peru and elsewhere, as more races are studied cytologically. In the intermediate and lowland areas there is chromosome evidence to indicate that mixtures between Andean and other types have occurred and also some lowland Bolivian races seem to be allied cytologically with knob patterns apparently concentrated in Venezuela and Chile. However, additional lowland races will need to be studied before these relationships become clear.

These preliminary data suggest that centers of specific knob patterns are still intact in certain areas, at least in South America. If this finally proves to be true, it would appear that precise information on knobs might become an even more important tool in tracing the history and evolution of maize in the Western Hemisphere. Before this can be attempted, however, a study of the type from which these data are taken will have to be extended to include the major races of maize of both South and Middle America.

TABLE 4. Number and position of chromosome knobs of eleven races of highland Bolivian maize.

Race	Number plants examined	Chromosome 7	Chromosome 6	Other knobs	Number B chromosomes
Confite Puneño	3	M–S [1]	very small [2]	0	2
		"	" "	0	0
		"	" "	0	3
Altiplano	3	M–S	very small	0	0
		"	" "	0	0
		"	" "	0	4
Kulli	4	M–S	very small	0	0
		"	" "	0	0
		"	" "	0	1
		"	" "	0	0
Huilcaparu	5	M–S	0	0	0
		"	very small	0	0
		"	" "	0	1
		"	0	0	0
		"	0	0	0
Checchi	7	M–S	very small	0	1
		"	" "	0	2
		"	" "	0	1
		"	" "	0	6
		"	" "	0	3
		"	" "	0	0
		"	" "	0	1
Paru	4	M–S	very small	0	0
		"	" "	0	0
		"	" "	0	0
		"	0	0	0
Chuspillu	5	M–S	very small	0	1
		"	" "	0	0
		"	" "	0	2
		"	" "	0	2
		"	0	0	0
Cuzco Boliviano	5	M–S	0	0	0
		"	0	0	0
		"	0	0	0
		"	0	0	1
		"	0	0	0
Uchuquilla	8	M–S	very small	0	1
		"	" "	0	0
		"	" "	0	0
		"	" "	0	0
		"	" "	0	0
		"	" "	0	3
		"	" "	0	1
		"	" "	0	0
Karapampa	4	M–S	0	0	3
		"	0	0	0
		"	very small	0	2
		"	" "	0	2

TABLE 4. Number and position of chromosome knobs of eleven races of highland Bolivian maize.—Continued

Race	Number plants examined	Chromo- some 7	Chromo- some 6	Other knobs	Number B chromo- somes
Niñuelo	8	M–S	very small	0	0
"		" "	" "	0	0
"		"	" "	0	0
"		"	" "	0	3
"		"	" "	0	2
"		"	" "	0	1
"		"	" "	0	0
"		"	" "	0	1

[1] Medium to small.
[2] Small knob in lower position in chromosome 6. All knobs in long arm if not otherwise stated.

METHODS OF CLASSIFICATION

In beginning the classification of the previously assembled collections, the three representative ears saved from each original collection were taken out of storage, each set of three labelled with its accession number. These ears were laid out on long tables in a large open shed which provided a good combination of protection from the elements, plenty of work space, and good illumination. Collections which looked similar were placed near each other on the same table, paying attention to color, texture, and size of grain; number of rows; and size and shape of ear. It was immediately apparent that several of the races previously described and illustrated by Cutler (Altiplano, Coroico, etc.) in his studies of Bolivian Maize (15) were present in the collections. With the assistance of Ing. Alexander Grobmann of La Molina, Peru and Sr. Pablo Daza of the Granja Tulio Ospina at Medellín, several other common varieties were distinguished and assembled. The remaining races were worked out by distinctive combinations of form and color, as for example, *Checchi,* small oval ears and kernels speckled blue on an off-white background.

Work was continued until a preliminary classification had been worked out using only the appearance of the ears themselves. The notes on location and altitudes of the original collections were then consulted. This on the whole confirmed previous judgments but in one case it demonstrated that two somewhat similar races had been confused and in others that certain classifications made

TABLE 5. Number and positions of chromosome knobs of non "Andean" races of Bolivian maize.

Races	Chromosome No.										
	1	2	3	4	5	6	7	8	9	10	B type
PISANKALLA [1]											
Coll. 344-1	0	Hetero. L.	0	Hetero. L.	Homo. med.	Hetero. Very small	Very small/med	Hetero. very L.	0	0	
Coll. 344-2	0	Hetero. L.	0	Hetero. L.	Homo. med.	Very small	0	0	0	0	
Coll. 864-1	0	Very small	0	0	Homo. med.	0	Homo. med.	Homo. very L.[2]	0	0	
Coll. 864-2	Hetero. Med. L.	0	0	Hetero. L.	Homo. med.	0	Hetero. med.	Homo. very L.	0	0	
Coll. 965-1	0	0	0	Homo. L.	Homo. med.	Hetero. small	Very small	Hetero. very L.	Homo., small end short arm	0	
Coll. 965-2	0	0	0	0	0	0	Very small	0	small end short arm	0	
Coll. 1106-1	0	0	0	Hetero. L.	0	0	Very small	Homo. very L.	0	0	
Coll. 1106-2	0	0	0	0	Hetero. med.	0	Very small	Hetero. very L.	0	0	
COROICO											
Coll. 992-1	0	0	0	0	0	Very small	Homo. med-small		0	0	
Coll. 992-2	0	Homo. med-small	0	(Homo.) L.	0	Very small	Homo. med-small		0	0	
Coll. 1035-1	0	0	0	0	Hetero. med-small	Very small	Homo. med-small		0	0	
Coll. 1035-2	0	0	0	0	0	Very small	Homo. med-small		0	0	
Coll. 1063	0	0	0	0	0	Very small	Homo. med-small		0	0	
Coll. 1071	0	0	0	0	0	Very small	Homo. med-small		0	0	
ENANO											
Coll. 1036-1	0	0	0	Hetero. L.	0	Homo. small	Homo. med-small		0	0	
Coll. 1036-2	0	0	0	0	0	Homo. small	Homo. med-small		0	0	
Coll. 1036-3	0	0	0	0	0	Homo. small	Homo. med-small		0	0	
Coll. 1036-4	0	0	0	0	0	Homo. small	Homo. med-small		0	0	
POJOSO CHICO											
Coll. 749	0	Homo. L.	0	0	0	0	Homo. med-small	0	Homo., L. end short arm	0	1
Coll. 755	0	Homo. L.	0	Hetero. L.	0	0	Homo. med-small	0	0	0	
Coll. 809	0	Homo. L.	0	Hetero	0	Homo. very small	Homo. med-small	0	0	0	
CHOLITO											
Coll. 705	0	(Homo.) L.[3]	0	0	0	Homo. med.	Homo. med-small	Homo. L.-upper pos. Hetero. small-lower pos.	Homo. small, end short arm	0	

34

TABLE 5.—Continued

Chromosome No.

Races	1	2	3	4	5	6	7	8	9	10	B type
Coll. 779–1	0	0	0	Homo. L.	0	Homo. med.	Med. small	0	0	0	
Coll. 779–2	0	0	0	Homo. L.	0	0	Med. small	Homo. L.	0	0	
Coll. 779–3	Hetero. Med. L.	Hetero. L.	0	Hetero. L.	0	0	Very small	Hetero. L.	0	0	2
Coll. 781–1	Hetero. Med. L.	0	0	0	0	Very small	Very small	Homo. med. L.	0	0	
Coll. 781–2	Homo. Med. L.	Homo. L.	0	Large	0	Very small	Very small	Large	0	0	
ARROCILLO											
Coll. 350	Homo. L., short arm	Homo. L.	Homo. L.	Homo. L.	Hetero. L.	Hetero. med.[3] lower pos. Hetero. med.-middle pos.[3]	Hetero. L. end short arm, L. long arm	Homo. L.-upper pos. Hetero. small-lower pos.	Homo. L. end short arm. L. long arm	0	
Coll. 711	0	Hetero. L.	Hetero. L.	Homo. L.	0	Hetero. very small-lower pos. Hetero. med.-middle pos.[3]	Homo. L. end short arm. Hetero. small long arm	0	Homo. med. end short arm. Hetero L. long arm	0	
Coll. 712	Homo. L.	Hetero. L.	0	Hetero. L.	Hetero. L.	Hetero. L.-lower pos. Hetero. med.-middle pos.[3]	Homo. med.	Hetero. L.-upper pos. Homo. small-lower pos.	Homo. med. end short arm. L. long arm	0	
PORORO											
Coll. 583–1	0	Homo. L.	Homo. L.	0	Homo. L.	Homo. med. Homo. med. small Homo. med.	Homo. L.	0	Homo. small-end short arm	0	
Coll. 583–2	0	Homo. L.	Homo. L.	0	Homo. L.	Homo. med. Homo. med. small Homo. med.	Homo. L.	0	Homo. small end short arm	0	
Coll. 806–1	0	Homo. L.	Homo. L.	0	0	Homo. med. Homo. med. small	Homo. L.	Homo. L.	Homo. med. small end short arm	0	
Coll. 806–2	0	Homo. L.	Homo. L.	0	0	Homo. med. small Homo. med. small	Homo. L.	Homo. L.	Homo. med. small end short arm	0	

EXPLANATION: All knobs on long arms unless otherwise noted.
Homo.—Homozygous knob.
Hetero.—Heterozygous knob.
Med.-small—Medium to small knob.
L.—Large.
Very small/Med—Homozygous but one chromosome with very small and other chromosome with med. knob.
( )—Probably homozygous.

[1] Pisankalla occurs at high altitudes but does not possess the knob pattern characteristic of other highland races.
[2] Heterozygous for inversion in short arm.
[3] Knob slender.

35

largely on slight color differences had ignored general similarities in form.

When the racial composition of the varieties was provisionally worked out, as many selections from each race as possible were planted for study, nearly always at more than one elevation. When the plants tasseled, they were examined repeatedly without reference to the ear notes. On the whole there was excellent agreement between judgments derived from the ears and those from examination of tassel, internode patterns, leaves and general aspect.

The photographs of the typical ears were then carefully compared with the plants grown from them. The three ears could frequently be rated one, two or three for a combination of distinctive characters such as row number and kernel shape. The plants were then examined as to what plant characters, if any, paralleled the observed sequence in ear shape. At other times the rows of plants were arranged in sequence for some plant character or combination of characters and were then compared with the photographs of the ears.

In this way it was possible to follow what George Box calls the itterative process of discovery. Hypotheses based on a study of the ears were checked by an examination of the plants. Hypotheses based on plant study could be confirmed by examining the ears. On the basis of these observations new and more inclusive hypotheses could be formed. When a combination of characters which tended to go together was found it could be recognized and used in working out the racial composition of the varieties.

For instance, it was found, as previously reported by Cutler (15), that there were various transitional intermediates between *Cuzco* and *Huilcaparu*. These races have been grown together for centuries in the same area. This was laboriously checked and re-checked in the plots, comparing scorings and measurements of the living plants with pictures of the original ears.

As compared with Huilcaparu, Cuzco has unpigmented, wider, less dented kernels on an ear with fewer row numbers. It also has smaller, narrower leaves and a straighter and more slender stalk and tassel, with fewer and more slender tassel branches. Repeated comparisons of the ears of Huilcaparu and Cuzco and their various intermediates demonstrated a definite association between wide leaves, stout stems, heavy tassels and high row numbers of colored, more dented kernels. This held for the various collections of *Cuzco* and *Huilcaparu* as well as for their various intermediates. After laboriously checking and rechecking, it was possible, with some confidence, to assign a large number of collections to *Cuzco*, to *Huilcaparu,* and to an intermediate (and variable) group.

Two further examples will illustrate something of the process by which the races were sifted out of the hundreds of collections. The *Morados* were originally picked out from the other varieties with strong kernel interlocking because of their dark color. This deep purple color is due to several genes and is known to be present from Peru to Arizona in a series of ancient varieties of corn used for coloring beverages or special breads and wafers made from corn. The Morados were found to be shorter than the other interlocked varieties, and somewhat intermediate between them and high altitude dye corns in still other characters. When the data on altitudes were consulted it was found that the Morados had been collected at an intermediate altitude, above the zone of the *Coroicos* and below that in which other dye corns are known.

To take another example, the *Enanos* were originally separated from the other small white popcorns because their ears had enlarged bases to which the upper end of the shank adhered so strongly that it could be broken off only with difficulty. This is a character common to the *Coroicos,* suggesting that in spite of the great difference in size the *Coroicos* might be related to the *Enanos.* The *Enanos* were then examined for interlocked grains and were found to have this character. Further study showed that both collections possessed streaks of purple coloring in the cobs and husks. Reference to the collectors' notes showed that it was a popcorn used as such and grown in openings in the jungle in much the same area as are the *Coroicos.* The variety was made an object of special study by Dr. G. Edward Nicholson Calle. He not only re-collected seed of it but found that it was commonly grown over wide areas in forest clearings in the Bolivian and Peruvian jungle.

CHARACTERS USED IN CLASSIFICATION

With slight modification the characters used in classifying the Bolivian races were those used previously in studies of the races of maize of Mexico (67) and Colombia (53). Since the system of measurement or scores of most of these characters has become standardized we are duplicating almost verbatim the description of characters found in the Colombian report. We feel the repetition is necessary since some workers interested in Bolivian maize may not have access to "Races of Maize in Colombia."

All measurements of ear characters were made on the original ears, thus these characters are from plants grown in their native habitats. All other characters were made on plants grown in Colombia either at "Tibaitatá" near Bogotá, at an elevation of 2.650 meters, at Medellín with an elevation of 1500 meters, at 1000 meters at Palmira or at Montería with an elevation of 50 meters. Using the collector's data as a guide an effort was made to grow the collections at the elevation to which they were best adapted. For comparative purposes, plant data used for the descriptions are those taken at Tibaitatá and Palmira. Plant data from Medellín and Palmira are also listed in separate tables.

VEGETATIVE CHARACTERS OF THE PLANT

Adaptation to Altitude—The dominant factor influencing the distribution of the Bolivian races of maize is altitude. Temperature in a country such as this is almost directly related to elevation, and it is largely for this reason that any given race can only be moved up and down within a certain range of elevation and still remain relatively well adapted to the environment.

Altitudes for most of the collections were accurately measured with an aneroid altimeter. Where this was not possible for a small percentage of the collections, the altitudes were taken from the best maps available.

Height of Plant—This character was obtained from one average plant of a typical collection grown at or near the elevation of its original habitat. The measurement was made from ground level to the base of the tassel.

Height to Ear—Ear height for the uppermost ear was not recorded directly in the field but was calculated from the internode measurements of typical collections and is presented in the appendix as such. These heights may not agree with ear heights represented on the internode diagram since the latter represent plants with modal number of internodes only.

Stem Diameter : Maximum and Minimum—The means by races for this character are averages of measurements made at the mid-point of the first internode above the ground on the main stalk. Also to obtain a picture of the relative shapes of the main stalk at the mid-point of the first internode, two measurements were taken at this point. One was taken of the maximum diameter and the other of the minimum. The relationship between the averages of the two serves to give a fairly good idea of the cross-sectional shape of the main stem slightly above ground level. Some races have slightly elliptically shaped stems; others have stems which are almost round; the majority have stems that fall somewhere between these two extremes in shape.

Length of Leaf—The mean for each typical collection is based on the measurement of a leaf from all normal plants in a plot. The measurements were made from the ligule to the tip on the leaf arising immediately below the ear-bearing node. The means of the representative collections were averaged to derive the racial means for this character.

Width of Leaf—The same procedure was followed as for length of leaf, the measurements being made at the mid-point in the length of each leaf.

Venation Index—The procedure described in the study of the races of Mexico (67) was used to derive this index. It consists of the quotient of the average number of veins counted at mid-point in the length of the leaf immediately below the upper ear-bearing node and the average width at the same point. The counts and measurements were made on all plants scored in each collection.

Number of Tillers—Actual counts were made on all plants scored. The means of the typical collections were averaged to derive the racial means. Tillers were also given a height score of *tall, medium* or *short*. Those scored *tall* were equal or sub-equal to the main culm. *Medium* were approximately one-half the height of the main culm and those scored *short* were less than one-half the height of the main culm.

Internode Patterns—After the model number of internodes for each race had been chosen as characteristic, the pattern was determined by using the measured length of successive internodes on all plants having that number of internodes. The results were then averaged and expressed in a diagram showing the pattern of relative internode lengths which also indicates the position of the uppermost ear of the plant. Numbers on the vertical scale in the diagrams represent lengths of each internode in centimeters. Numbers at the base of the diagram represent the number of internodes from the base upwards.

CHARACTERS OF THE TASSEL

Length of the Peduncle—The distance between the terminal node of the main culm and the lowermost primary branch of the tassel.

Length of Branching Area—The distance between the basal and uppermost primary branches of the tassel.

Length of the Central Spike—Distance between the uppermost primary branch and the apex of the tassel.

Length of the Uppermost Primary Branch—Self explanatory.

Length of the Best Developed Primary Branch—Usually the lowermost primary branch except in some plants with strongly inserted tassels.

Number of Secondary and Teritary Branches on Best Developed Primary—Self explanatory.

Total Number of Primary Branches with Secondaries—Self explanatory.

Total Number of Primary Branches with Teritaries—Self explanatory.

Total Number of Primary Branches—Self explanatory.

CHARACTER OF THE EAR

EXTERNAL CHARACTERS

Ear Length—The measurements were made on all normally developed ears in the collections.

Mid-ear Diameter—The diameters of the same ears used to determine ear length were measured with calipers at the mid-point of their length.

Row Number—Actual counts were made of the number of rows of grain on the same ears used for length and diameter determinations.

Number of Husks—The husks (modified leaf sheaths) surrounding the ear were counted on the principal ear of all plants scored. The data are expressed as an average number per plant. The number of condensed husk nodes of the shank were also determined by counting the number of apparent nodes and comparing it with the number of husks produced.

Kernel Width—The width of ten kernels taken from near the middle of the ear and laid side by side was measured in millimeters.

Kernel Thickness—The thickness of ten consecutive kernels in a row near the mid-point of an ear was measured in millimeters with metal calipers. The measurements were made while the kernels were on the ear.

Kernel Length—The same ten kernels were measured when laid end to end.

Kernel Denting—This is a visual estimate recorded on an arbitrary scale: from 0=maximum to 5=none. Observations were individually recorded for the same ears as for the above characters, the scores being averaged.

Kernel Hardness—Visual estimates were made on the total sample of ears of each collection and these were recorded on an arbitrary scale from 1 (hard) to 5 (soft).

INTERNAL CHARACTERS

The measurements and observations on these characters which will be described below are presented in Table 9 and the cross-sectional diagrams of the ears of each race based on these measurements and observations are included with the descriptions.

Cob Diameter—This was measured from the center of the upper surface of the upper glume on one side of the cob to the corresponding point on the upper surface of a glume directly opposite.

Rachis Diameter—This was measured with calipers on the lower half of the broken ear. The measurement was made from the base of an upper glume on one side of the cob to the base of an upper glume directly opposite. Since the base of the glume is usually somewhat below the rim of the cupule, this measurement does not represent the maximum diameter of the rachis but rather its diameter to the points at which the upper glume arises.

Cob/rachis Index—This is computed by dividing the diameter of the cob by the diameter of the rachis.

Glume/kernel Index—This index gives a measure of the length of the glume in relation to the length of the kernel. It is computed by subtracting the diameter of the rachis from the diameter of the cob and dividing the figure obtained by twice the average length of kernel.

Cupule Hairs—The cupule is almost invariably hairy. The hairs vary both in number and length from a few short prickles to many long, sometimes appressed hairs. They also vary greatly from race to race in this distribution within and about the cupule. The variation is so extensive that the characteristic alone is of little value. It may, however, be useful when considered with other characteristics and employed as part of the total description. Hairiness is scored by numbers from 0=none to 2=profuse.

Lower Glume: Texture—The texture of the lower glumes is estimated by probing or puncturing with a dissecting needle. In some races the glumes are chaffy, often with considerable areas towards the margins of thin transparent material resembling tissue paper. In other races the glumes are fleshy and thickened, but soft, and yield easily to the needle point. In still other races the glumes are distinctly indurated and are difficult to puncture. Induration is scored by numbers, from 0=none to 2=strong.

Lower Glume: Hairiness—The hairs of the lower glumes vary in number, length and position. Hairs are found almost universally on the upper margins of the glume. These vary from a few short hairs to many long, soft hairs. The surface of the glume proper may be completely glabrous. More commonly a few hairs are found at the base or toward the lateral margins of the glumes. In general, the hairiness of the lower glume is not in itself a satisfactory diagnostic character, since there is often considerable variation within a race. Considered with other characteristics, however, it has some usefulness. Hairiness of the glumes is scored by numbers, from 0=none to 2=profuse.

Lower Glume: Shape of the Glume Margin—The upper margin of the glume varies in shape from race to race. The margin is rarely truncate and is usually more or less indented. The indentation may be luniform (crescent-shaped), more or less broadly angulate (wedge-shaped), sinuate (undulate or wavy), or cordate (heart-shaped). The shape of the margins is fairly uniform among different ears of the same race.

Upper Glume: Hairiness—Hairs on the upper glume, like those on the lower, vary in number, length and position and are scored in the same way.

Rachis Induration—The surface of the rachis tissue varies in the degree of induration. This is probably a matter of degree to which the tissue is schlerenchymatized. An estimate of the induration of the rachis, like that of the lower glume, can be made by probing the rachis tissues with a dissecting needle. The induration has been arbitrarily scored as follows: 0=no induration, 1=slight, 2=intermediate, 3=strong.

PHYSIOLOGICAL AND GENETIC CHARACTERS

The characters included in this category (Table 10) are as follows:

Maturity—The number of days from planting to silking was used as a measure of maturity. The date of silking for each collection was recorded when one-half of the plants in a plot containing 50 to 60 plants had put forth silks.

Corn Rust—Three species of rust, *Puccinia sorghi, P. polysora* and *Angiospora zeae,* have been identified on maize grown in Colombia. Since *P. sorghi* is of major importance and the other two species are relatively unimportant, only one rust note was taken with respect to the degree of resistance or susceptibility on the scale of 1 to 5, 1 being highly resistant and 5 highly susceptible. The various races of maize exhibited considerable differences in reaction to *P. sorghi.*

Helminthosporium—This disease, like rust, is very common and damaging in parts of Colombia. To date the species of *Helminthosporium* prevalent in Colombia have not been identified with any degree of certainty, although it is now fairly clear that *H. turcicum* largely predominates with *H. carbonum* being present, but to a minor degree. All of the collections have been scored for resistance or susceptibility to this disease although in this report no distinction is made between two species of leaf blight. The scale used for recording the visual estimates was from 1=resistant to 5=susceptible.

Pilosity—Pubescence in Table 10 is arbitrarily scored from 1 to 5 for both frequency and intensity, the higher number indicating the stronger pubescence. Texture of pubescence was scored arbitrarily into classes of hard, medium and soft.

Plant Color—Many high-altitude races of Mexico, Guatemala and Colombia have strongly colored leaf sheaths. This color is sometimes due to the B factor on chromosome 2, sometimes to one of the R alleles on chromosome 10, and sometimes results from both. The empirical scores in Table 10, ranging from 1 to 5, do not distinguish between these two genes for color. Color, like pubescence, reaches its maximum in the high-altitude corns. A visual estimate was made in a plot of from 50 to 60 plants of each collection for both frequency and intensity of the plant color to arrive at an arbitrary score. Purple plant color was scored separately using a scale of 1 to 5 with 5 representing the most intensive plant color.

Lemma Color—The color of red-cobbed corn is in the lemma, but there are other colors in the lemma as well. No attempt was made to distinguish between colors due to the different genes involved, and only the presence or absence of color was noted on 10 to 15 ears of each original collection. This is expressed (Table 10) as percentage of ears with lemma color among the ears which were scored for this character.

Glume Color—Lacking anthocyanin, the glumes are white, buff or brownish. Anthocyanin coloration may be red, cherry or purple. The frequency of glume color is recorded as a percentage of the ears studied.

Mid-cob Color—Midcob color affects the tissues between the pith and epidermis of the rachis. It is seen only when the cob is broken and for this reason its widespread distribution in Latin American races has been largely overlooked. The data recorded represent an average percentage of the ears that had midcob color. Approximately ten ears of each collection were read for this character.

Pith Color—Expressed in percentage of the ears of the original collections that showed color in the pith, regardless of its nature. The genetic nature of pith color is not known.

Aleurone Color—Expressed in percentage of the ears of the original collections that had aleurone color, irrespective of its nature.

Pericarp Color—Scored on the ears of the original collections and expressed in percentage.

DESCRIPTION OF RACES

In the pages that follow, thirty-two races of Bolivian maize are described. These are arranged roughly according to altitude, from highest to lowest. It should be made clear in the beginning that our classification into more or less distinct races should in nowise be considered the final answer to the race problem in Bolivian maize. Only two of the authors, Brown and Nicholson, have had opportunity to observe and study Bolivian maize in its native habitat. In each of these cases, the time at the authors' disposal was far too limited to provide more than a superficial insight into the maize and the people who grow it. Neither has there been time or facilities at our disposal to conduct experiments in inbreeding and crossing with this group of corns. As demonstrated for Mexico and Colombia, this is a most useful tool in the study of relationships. When such information is available it may alter the classification here presented.

Most of the previous studies in this series have placed considerable emphasis on the origin and relationships of the races described (53, 67). It will be immediately apparent to the reader that these subjects are either omitted here or are treated in a very tentative manner. Although among Bolivian maize there are a few obvious relationships to races which have been previously described from other areas and certain obvious relationships among Bolivian races themselves, we feel that knowledge of these corns is as yet far too incomplete for effective discussion of the origin of the Bolivian races.

Finally our method of presenting race descriptions differs somewhat from that used in the earlier papers of this series. Instead of repeating in the descriptions the summarized information contained in tabular form in the Appendix, we shall merely describe for each race what we consider its characteristic morphological features for kernel, ear, tassel, stem and leaves. In addition to the tabular data, the descriptions will be further supplemented with photographs of typical ears, internode diagrams, cross sectional ear diagrams and distribution maps.

RACES OF MAIZE

CONFITE PUÑEÑO

Ear Photograph,   Figure 2
Ear Diagram,   Figure 3
Internode Diagram, Figure 4
Distribution Map,   Figure 5

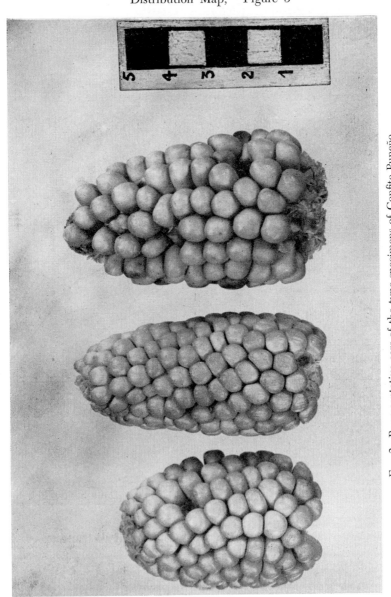

FIG. 2. Representative ears of the type specimens of Confite Puñeño.
(*Centimeter scale is used on all photographs.*)

Mean altitude of type specimens 3730 meters. Others 2160–3993 meters. Typical collections: Bov. 892, Bov. 822, Bov. 661, Bov. 891, Bov. 824, Bov. 882♯. Ears with small, round flinty kernels; yellow endosperm; colored pericarp frequent; blue aleurone; mostly white cob; central spike of tassel—heavy, flat. Tassel branches short, heavy, stiff; branching at approximately 60° angle. Tassel exsertion long, about equalling the length of the sheath of the upper leaf. Some plants without condensation, others with heavy and regular condensation in tassel branches. Node exsertion—all included. Leaves narrow. Ears attached very low on plant. Stem—slender. Plant color—black purple. Name refers to a confection from Puna.

Fig. 3. Ear cross-section diagram of Confite Puneño.

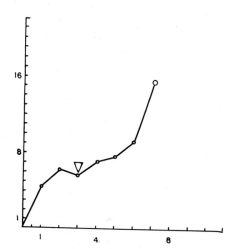

Fig. 4. Internode pattern of Confite Puneño.

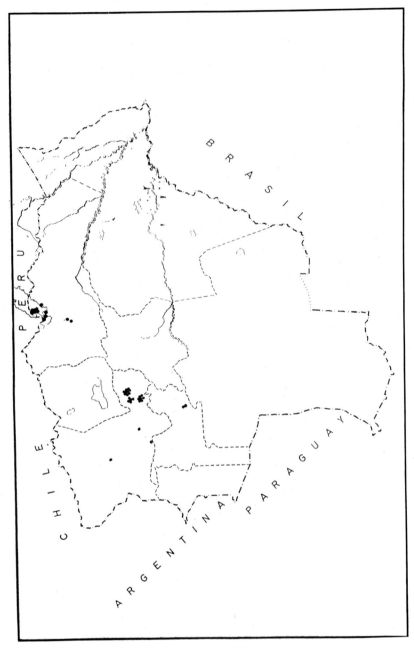

Fig. 5. The distribution of Confite Puneño.

ALTIPLANO

Ear Photograph,	Figure 6
Ear Diagram,	Figure 7
Internode Diagram,	Figure 8
Distribution Map,	Figure 9

Fig. 6. Representative ears of the type specimens of Altiplano.

Mean altitude of type specimens 2980 meters. Others 1900–3800 meters. Typical collections: Bov. 494, Bov. 730‡, Bov. 903‡, Bov. 1002‡. Extremely variable; high row numbers; mostly floury endosperm; pericarp red; variegated; purple aleurone; purple dotted; colorless; white or red cob; kernels longer than wide, somewhat pointed. Husks vary from loose to somewhat tight. Central spike of tassel—arching. Tassel branches—slender arching. Slightly exserted tassels. Node exsertion—well included. Little condensation in tassel. Leaves broad. Ears placed low on plant. Plant color—dark purple. Stem—stout. Frequent long pedicels and long sterile zone in tassel. Glumes on lower tassel branches more or less broad but with long slender apices. Tassels disproportionately large for size of plants, in contrast to Confite Puneño which has small tassels on very small plants. Altiplano was the last of the small varieties to tassel and is very late maturing for its size. The name Altiplano was first applied by Cutler (15) to similar corns distributed in the high Andes from Argentina and Chile to Ecuador. Among the corns we have examined in the germ plasm bank in Colombia, varieties similar to Altiplano are found in both the Chilean and Peruvian collections.

Fig. 7. Ear cross-section diagram of Altiplano.

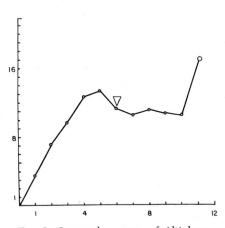

Fig. 8. Internode pattern of Altiplano.

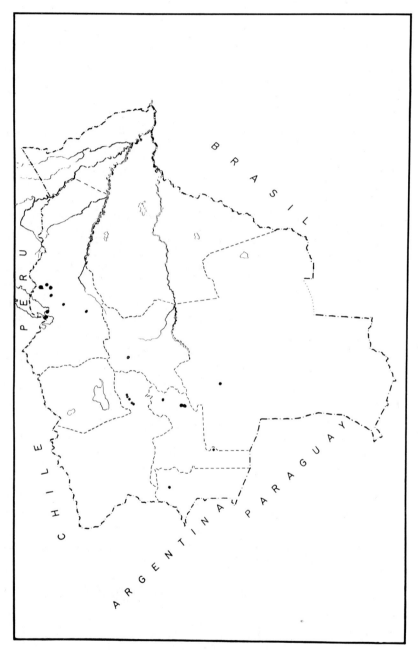

Fig. 9. The distribution of Altiplano.

RACES OF MAIZE

PATILLO

Ear Photograph,   Figure 10
Ear Diagram,   Figure 11
Internode Diagram, Figure 12
Distribution Map, Figure 13

Fɪɢ. 10. Representative ears of the type specimens of Patillo.

Mean altitude of type specimens 3275 meters. Others 2600–2660 meters. Typical collections: Bov. 493, Bov. 823, Bov. 589, Bov. 832♯, Bov. 502♯. Ears small, almost round to conical. 12 to 16 rows of yellow, nearly round, flinty kernels; white or red cob; slender tough shank. Ears quite uniform within collections. Central spike of tassel heavy, often flat. Tassel branches short and stiff. Tassel exsertion—all exserted. Node exsertion—all included. Ears placed low on plant usually at second and third nodes. Plant color–sun red to purple. Stems slender. Tassel branches with broad rachis and very condensed spikelets. No distichous tassels. Glumes large and broad, blunt pointed. Prevailing broad ligules. As grown at Tibaitatá, in Colombia, Patillo was even shorter than Altiplano and was more badly damaged by *Helminthosporium*.

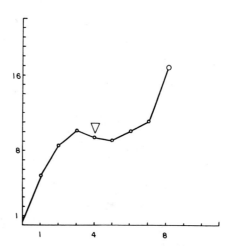

FIG. 11. Ear cross-section diagram of Patillo.

FIG. 12. Internode pattern of Patillo.

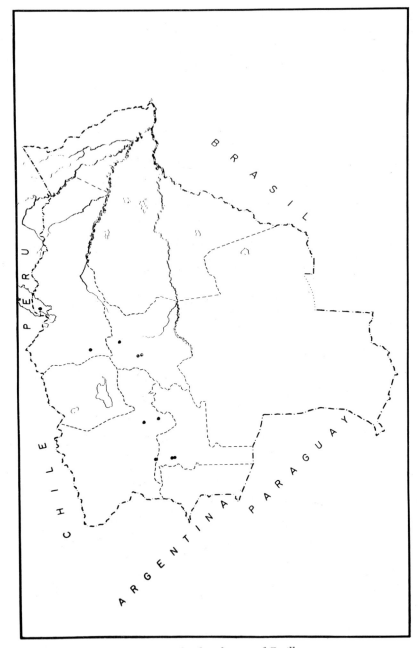

Fig. 13. The distribution of Patillo.

KCELLO

Fɪɢ. 14. Representative ears of the type specimens of Kcello.

Mean altitude of type specimens 3560 meters. Others 2000–3560 meters. Typical collections: Bov. 1027, Bov. 948, Bov. 325, Bov. 514♯, Bov. 848. Ears show more tendency toward uniform rows than do those of Patillo; straighter, fewer rows and with considerable similarity to the race Uchuquilla, to be described later. Ears have 8 to 10 rows or more of yellow, flinty kernels. White or red cob. Ears with straight and pronounced taper. Central spike of tassel arching and slender. Tassel branches—slender, arching. Tassels all exserted. Nodes frequently exserted. Leaves—broad. Ear placement variable, from low to high. Plant color variable, from red to purple. Stem more slender and taller than anything in three preceding races. Early maturity. Ligules not as broad as in Patillo. Nodes are frequently exserted from the sheath. Approximately one plant in ten has distichous tassel. Name in Quechuan means yellow.

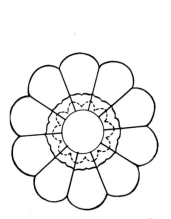

Fig. 15. Ear cross-section diagram of Kcello.

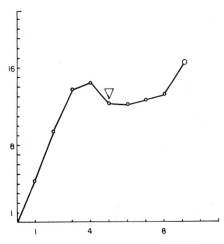

Fig. 16. Internode pattern of Kcello.

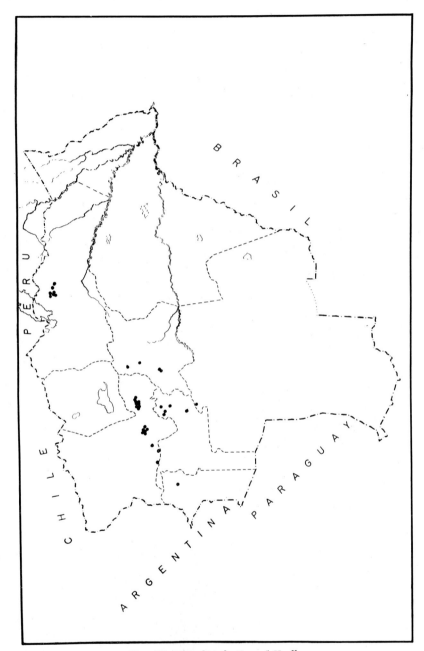

Fig. 17. The distribution of Kcello.

RACES OF MAIZE

KULLI

Ear Photographs,   Figure 18
Ear Diagram,   Figure 19
Internode Diagram, Figure 20
Distribution Map,   Figure 21

Fig. 18. Representative ears of the type specimens of Kulli.

Mean altitude of type specimens 3560 meters. Others 2000–3500 meters. Typical collections: Bov. 473, Bov. 1004, Bov. 486, Bov. 844♯, Bov. 734♯. A dye corn with short ears of hand grenade shape. Cherry pericarp and purple aleurone; large, more or less round to slightly pointed kernels with floury endosperm. Cobs red or white, attached to slender shanks. Both central spike and primary tassel branches sub-arching; tassels all exserted. Internodes occasionally exserted. Leaves more or less straight sided and unruffled. Plants of dark purple color with slender stems. Uniform within varieties, but varying between varieties.

Fig. 19. Ear cross-section diagram of Kulli.

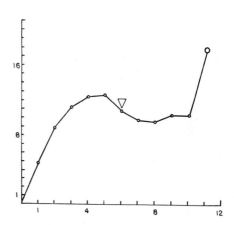

Fig. 20. Internode pattern of Kulli.

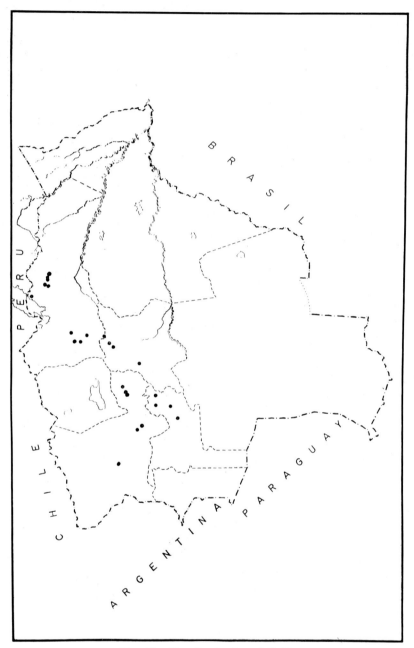

Fig. 21. The distribution of Kulli.

HUILCAPARU

Ear Photographs,   Figure 22
Ear Diagram,   Figure 23
Internode Diagram, Figure 24
Distribution Map,   Figure 25

FIG. 22. Representative ears of the type specimens of Huilcaparu.

Mean altitude of type specimens 2680 meters. Others 1400–3600 meters. Typical collections: Bov. 471, Bov. 762, Bov. 574, Bov. 685‡, Bov. 652‡. Mostly 12 row ears which are long and with large cobs. Kernels rounded at top and long with slight taper; floury or flinty; brown pericarp and purple aleurone. Brown or brown-red cob color. Central spike heavy and arching; primary tassel branches arching and stiff; tassels mostly exserted although a few included. Nodes all included. Leaves wide and slightly ruffled. Ears place above midpoint of stem. Plants tall, stout and light to strong sun red in color. Multiple leaf blades frequent at base of lowest apparent tassel branches. Later in maturity than any Bolivian high altitude race except Chuspillu. Leaves large, wide, lax and light green. Tassel branches usually longest at second or higher node above the base so that if the tips of all branches were connected with a line it would form an inverted heart. Central spike of tassel usually 3 to 4 sided, occasionally flattened just below tip.

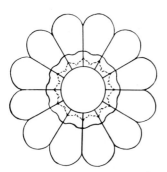

FIG. 23. Ear cross-section diagram of Huilcaparu.

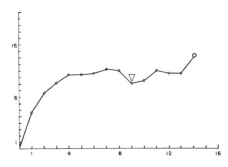

FIG. 24. Internode pattern of Huilcaparu.

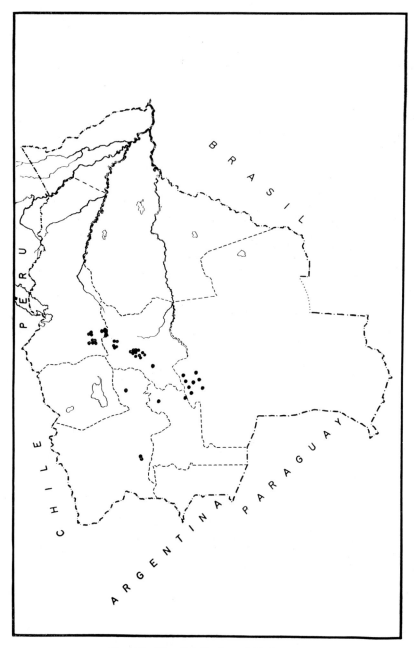

Fɪɢ. 25. The distribution of Huilcaparu.

CHAKE-SARA

Fig. 26. Representative ears of the type specimens of Chake-Sara.

Mean altitude of type specimens 2412 meters. Others 1900–2250 meters. Typical collections: Bov. 439, Bov. 520, Bov. 389, Bov. 413♯, Bov. 952. Medium sized ear with 10 to 12 or more rows of rounded or slightly tapered, white, flinty kernels. Ears rounded at butt. Cobs mostly white, few red. Central spike and primary branches of tassel arching; tassel well exserted. Ear placement low to medium height. Leaves short. Plant color slight to strong sun red. Varying within collections for ear height, otherwise remarkably consistent in plant type. Sara means maize and chake refers to a typical soup of the area made of maize, potatoes, etc.

FIG. 27. Ear cross-section diagram of Chake-Sara.

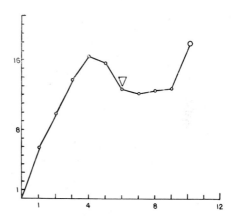

FIG. 28. Internode pattern of Chake-Sara.

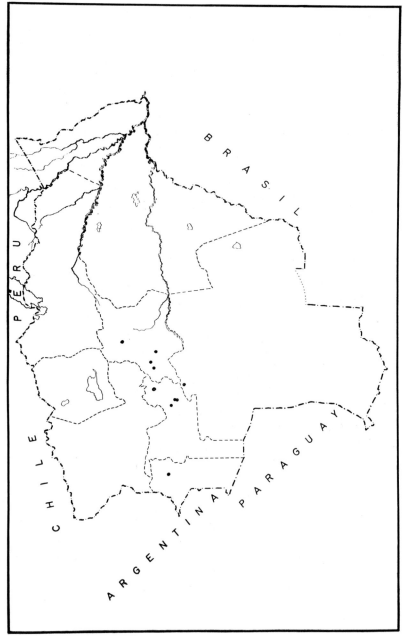

Fig. 29. The distribution of Chake-Sara.

AYSUMA

Fig. 30. Representative ears of the type specimens of Aysuma.

Mean altitude of type specimens 2892 meters. Others 2000–3560 meters. Typical collections: Bov. 331, Bov. 1030; Bov. 443, Bov. 936♯, Bov. 968♯. Ears medium size and slightly tapered; few irregular kernels (low degree of multiplication); kernels medium sized, red in color and partly white capped; some kernels slightly pointed. Cob of medium red color. Shank slender. Central spike of tassel slightly arching to upright; primary branches stiff but arching; tassels all exserted. Internodes slightly exserted. Leaves stiff. Ear placement low to medium. Stem stocky, sun red to purple in color, generally small and frequently with two or more ears. Leaves stiff, upper ones tending to stand out horizontally from stem; leaves with broad ligules. Tassels stiff, tending, even when dry, to arch in one direction.

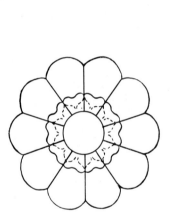

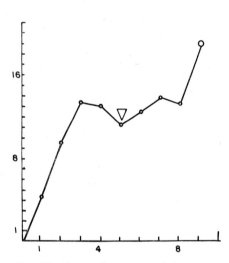

FIG. 31. Ear cross-section diagram of Aysuma.

FIG. 32. Internode pattern of Aysuma.

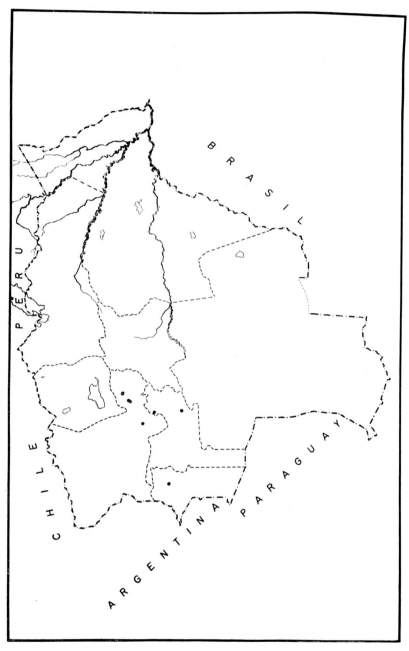

Fig. 33. The distribution of Aysuma.

RACES OF MAIZE

PATILLO GRANDE

Ear Photographs,   Figure 34
Ear Diagram,   Figure 35
Internode Diagram, Figure 36
Distribution Map,   Figure 37

Fig. 34. Representative ears of the type specimens of Patillo Grande.

Mean altitude of type specimens 2325 meters. Others 2378–2650 meters. Typical collections: Bov. 492, Bov. 501, Bov. 649, Bov. 714, Bov. 847. Ears medium large, tapering with more or less differentiated butt; kernels yellow, flinty, rounded; 12 rows; considerable multiplication. Cobs dark red to light red, few white, attached to slender shanks. Central spike of tassel arching; primary tassel branches medium long and arching. Tassels all exserted. Internodes slightly to well exserted. Leaves few and wide. Ear placement near middle of plant. Plant color semi-red to semi-purple. Stem short and stocky with two or three ears and with internodes somewhat zigzag. Very wide auricles. Some plants with very long central spikes. Longest tassel branches frequently two or three nodes up from base of tassel.

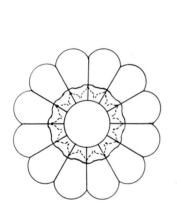

Fig. 35. Ear cross-section diagram of Patillo Grande.

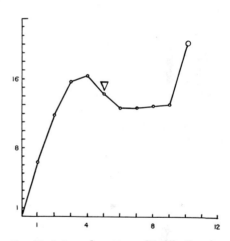

Fig. 36. Internode pattern of Patillo Grande.

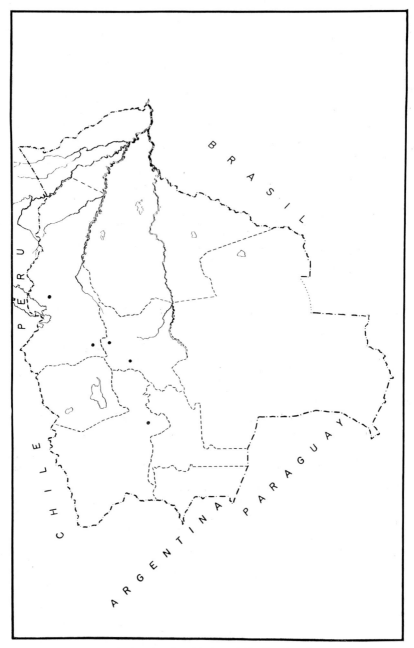

Fɪɢ. 37. The distribution of Patillo Grande.

CHECCHI

Ear Photographs,   Figure 38
Ear Diagram,   Figure 39
Internode Diagram, Figure 40
Distribution Map, Figure 41

FIG. 38. Representative ears of the type specimens of Checchi.

Mean altitude of type specimens 2520 meters. Others 2160–2750 meters. Typical collections: Bov. 421, Bov. 308, Bov. 840, Bov. 833♯, Bov. 320♯. Ears medium small with 14 to 16 rows of round conical kernels of floury endosperm. Ears somewhat tapered. Mostly dotted aleurone, segregating for white. Cob color white or red. Shank slender to very slender. Central spike of tassel heavy, some flattened. Tassel branches stiff and arching. Tassels all exserted. Internodes mostly inserted. Leaves wide, straight edged. Ears placed low on plant. Plants semi-red to purple in color. Stems stiff. The plants, like the ears, differ little within collections and considerably between them. Even the non-typical collections are uniform. This suggests that these are indeed "specialty" corns which have been kept going at separate haciendas for their distinctive color and probably for their floury texture. Dr. Martín Cárdenas states (personal communication) that Checchi is used almost exclusively for parched corn. The name refers to a grey color on a white background.

Fig. 39. Ear cross-section diagram of Checchi.

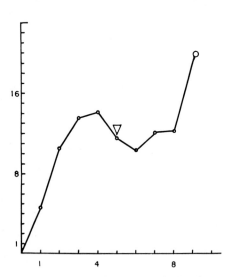

Fig. 40. Internode pattern of Checchi.

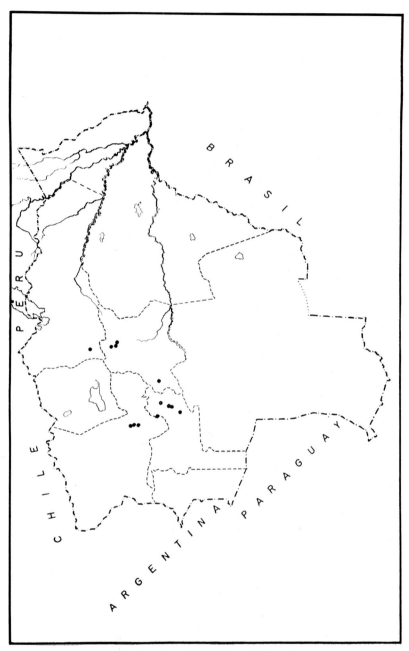

FIG. 41. The distribution of Checchi.

PARU

Ear Photographs,   Figure 42
Ear Diagram,   Figure 43
Internode Diagram, Figure 44
Distribution Map, Figure 45

FIG. 42. Representative ears of the type specimens of Paru.

Mean altitude of typical specimens 2800 meters. Others 2800 meters. Typical collections: Bov. 724, Bov. 528, Bov. 718. Ears are hand grenade shaped to almost spherical; strongly compressed by husks. Kernels are long and tapered and some are strongly beaked. Row numbers 16 or more with much multiplication. Aleurone mostly purple or dotted. Cobs are proportionately large. Central spike of the tassel is heavy, erect to arched. Tassel branches arching, stiff and heavy. Most tassels are exserted although few included. Internodes all included. Leaves are wide, drooping and without graceful curve. Ear placement is near the middle of the plant. Plants are semi-red to semi-purple. Stem is stout with large, loose sheaths.

Fig. 43. Ear cross-section diagram of Paru.

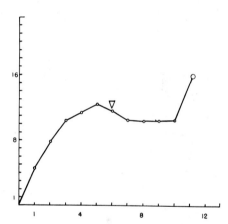

Fig. 44. Internode pattern of Paru.

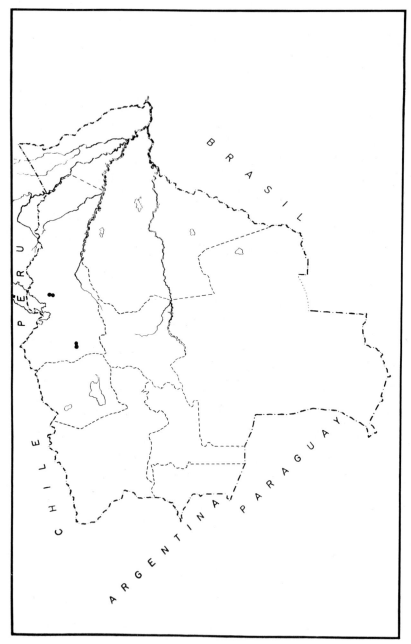

Fig. 45. The distribution of Paru.

CHUSPILLU

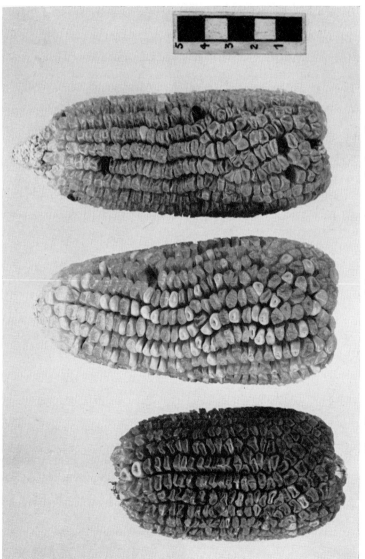

Fig. 46. Representative ears of the type specimens of Chuspillu.

Mean altitude type specimens 2490 meters. Others 1098–3600 meters. Typical collections: Bov. 478, Bov. 458, Bov. 883, Bov. 846♯, Bov. 360♯. Ears with sugary endosperm except for contaminating pollinations; none as spherical as the classical Peruvian extremes; conical to short cylindrical; 18 to 30 rows. Cobs large. Kernels pale to deep yellow; non-sugary kernels show tapering or slight beaking. Cobs white. Strong husk compression. Central spike of tassel very heavy; tassel branches heavy and arching. Some included tassels. Some exserted internodes. Leaves wide. Ear placement variable but usually near middle of plant. Plant color light to strong semi-red. Stem stout. Latest of all Bolivian varieties to tassel at "Tibaitatá." Plant height variable within cultures. Very high degree of multiplication and condensation. Some tassel branches so condensed that they look like central spikes. Second and third tassel branches better developed than the lowest one. Used mostly for parching when mature and dry. Never used as green corn. Used also for chicha but is scarce in all markets in Bolivia. Chicha made from Chuspillu is more expensive and reportedly contains a higher percentage of alcohol than that made from other kinds of maize.

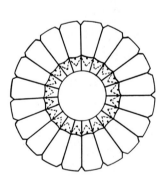

Fig. 47. Ear cross-section diagram of Chuspillu.

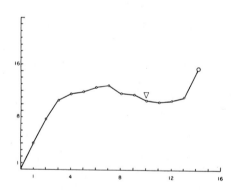

Fig. 48. Internode pattern of Chuspillu.

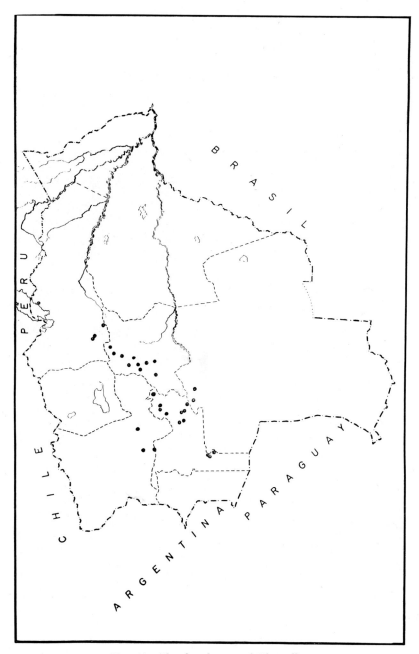

Fig. 49. The distribution of Chuspillu.

RACES OF MAIZE

CUZCO BOLIVIANO

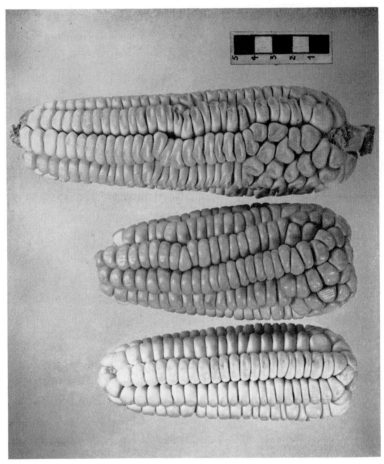

Fig. 50. Representative ears of the type specimens of Cuzco Boliviano.

Mean altitude of type specimens 2650 meters. Others 2000–2720 meters. Typical collections: Bov. 752, Bov. 482, Bov. 725, Bov. 540♯, Bov. 1137♯. This race is typical of the classical Cuzco of Peru. Ears eight-rowed with slight multiplication; ears of medium length. Kernels very large—the largest kernels we have seen from Bolivia are not however as large as the largest from Peru. Kernels circular to tapered; soft white starchy; slight dent or none. Cobs white. Ears rounded off at base by strong husk compression. Central spike of tassel slender, upright and arching. Tassel branches slender and sub-arching. Tassels all exserted (some very much so). Internodes mostly included. Narrow leaves. Stem slender. Plant color medium to strong semi-red. Slender, long internodes. Used as a boiled maize—kernels eaten individually.

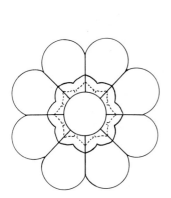

Fig. 51. Ear cross-section diagram of Cuzco Boliviano.

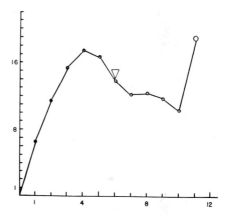

Fig. 52. Internode pattern of Cuzco Boliviano.

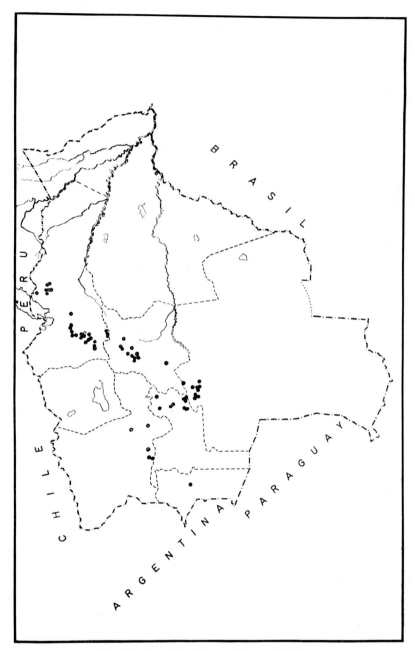

FIG. 53. The distribution of Cuzco Boliviano.

CUZCO—HUILCAPARU

Ear Photographs, Figure 54
Distribution Map, Figure 55

FIG. 54. Representative ears of the type specimens of Cuzco-Huilcaparu.

Cuzco and Huilcaparu are two of the commonest highland Bolivian races. The two occupy the same area and undoubtedly have hybridized with each other over long periods of time. As a consequence, any collection of high altitude corn from Bolivia will contain many types which are more or less intermediate between Cuzco and Huilcaparu. Because of the prevalence of these types we are including them as a race. Huilcaparu is uniform from sample to sample among the collections. Cuzco, though maintaining purity within the samples, has no great uniformity of ear or plant type even among the "typicos." The collections of it apparently differ in the extent to which the wide Cuzco-like grain has been selected. The Cuzcos seem to be varying mostly for introduced amounts of dwarfness and smaller ears. The intermediates include not only plants which are intermediate between Cuzco and Huilcaparu but others have yellow endosperm and show obvious resemblances to Patillo as well as to Cuzco and Huilcaparu. This is the most complex and heterogeneous set of collections of all of those made in Bolivia.

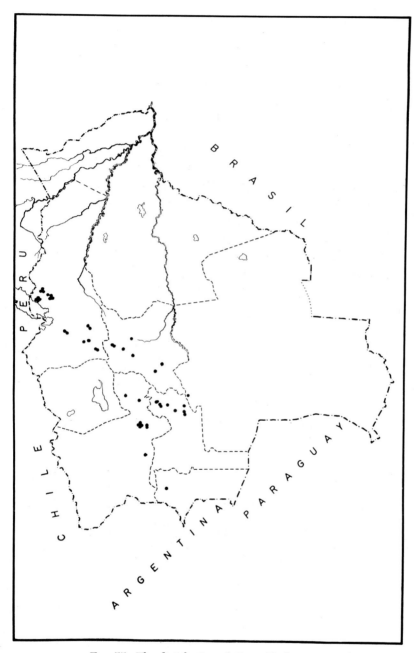

Fig. 55. The distribution of Cuzco-Huilcaparu.

RACES OF MAIZE

PISANKALLA

Fig. 56. Representative ears of the type specimens of Pisankalla.

Mean altitude of type specimens 2238 meters. Others 900–3560 meters. Typical collections: Bov. 864, Bov. 344, Bov. 760, Bov. 1106♯, Bov. 965♯. Ears slender with 16 or more rows of white, pointed, pop kernels. Some ears with strongly beaked kernels. Cobs white. Strong shank for size of ear. Central spike of tassel upright to arching. Tassel branches arching and with broad tips. Tassels all exserted. Few internodes exserted. Leaves narrow at base with small auricles and fine, evenly waved edges. Plants mostly green. Some collections characterized by tillers with tassel ears and silking tassels. Plants 3 to 5 feet in height but tassels small for size of plant. Plants very ungraceful and irregular in appearance.

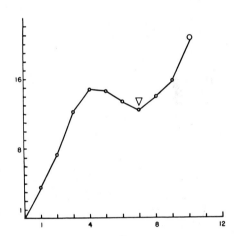

FIG. 57. Ear cross-section diagram of Pisankalla.

FIG. 58. Internode pattern of Pisankalla.

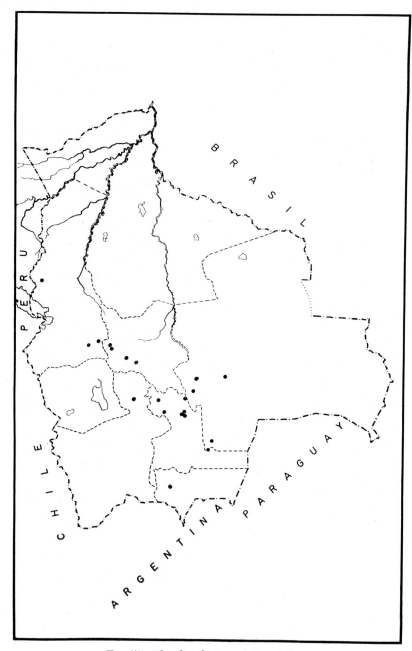

Fig. 59. The distribution of Pisankalla.

UCHUQUILLA

Fig. 60. Representative ears of the type specimens of Uchuquilla.

Mean altitude of type specimens 2165 meters. Others 1150–3420 meters. Typical collections: Bov. 869, Bov. 318, Bov. 303, Bov. 954♯, Bov. 1132♯. Uchuquilla shows obvious relationship in color and form to Karapampa. Ears 8-rowed, orange to red flints. Kernels rounded to slightly tapered. Cobs red or white. Bronze aleurone common. Ears slightly tapered with straight kernel rows. Compared to Karapampa, this race is taller, stouter, has more zig-zag internodes, more deep colors, more tassel branches, wider and less graceful leaves.

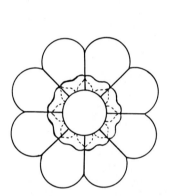

Fig. 61. Ear cross-section diagram of Uchuquilla.

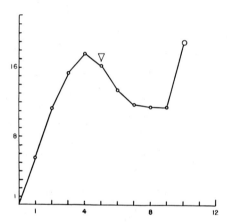

Fig. 62. Internode pattern of Uchuquilla.

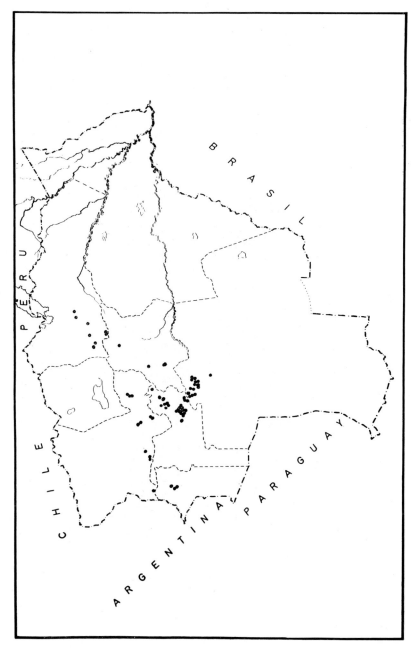

Fig. 63. The distribution of Uchuquilla.

KARAPAMPA

Fɪɢ. 64. Representative ears of the type specimens of Karapampa.

Mean altitude of type specimens 2123 meters. Others 1800–2160 meters. Typical collections: Bov. 422, Bov. 978, Bov. 961, Bov. 966♯. Slender cylindrical eared 8 to 10 rowed pop-flints. Kernels slightly to strongly tapered, never beaked. Orange or red color. Slender shanks. Differs from previous race in having smaller, more cylindrical cobs, smaller and more tapered kernels, harder kernels. Central spike of tassel arched to erect; tassel branches stiff. Some tassels exserted. Most internodes exserted. Ears placed near middle of plant. Plant color medium to light sun red. Stems with long internodes. Plants similar to those of Great Plains of the United States. Tiny upright tassel branches at base of tassel quite common.

Fig. 65. Ear cross-section diagram of Karapampa

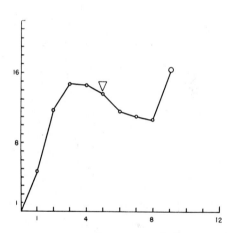

Fig. 66. Internode pattern of Karapampa.

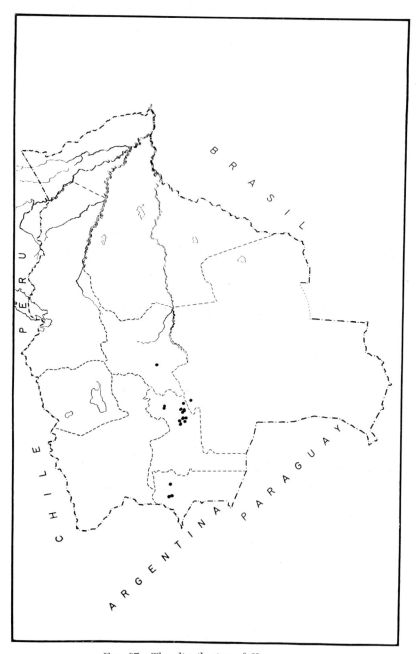

Fig. 67. The distribution of Karapampa.

ARGENTINO

Ear Photographs,   Figure 68
Ear Diagram,   Figure 69
Internode Diagram, Figure 70
Distribution Map,   Figure 71

Fig. 68. Representative ears of the type specimens of Argentino.

Mean altitude of type specimens 1568 meters. Others 500–2720 meters. Typical collections: Bov. 918, Bov. 469, Bov. 920. Argentino is apparently a commercial, improved corn. Ears are long, cylindrical with 10 to 12 straight rows. Kernels are rounded, very wide with long transverse dent and strongly white capped. Kernels never beaked or pointed. Medium to large shank. White cob. Plants extremely tall with rather thick stem and wide leaves in comparison to their length. Stems predominantly green with a slight degree of sun red color and a lesser degree of purple plant color. Leaf sheaths have an appreciable amount of stiff pubescence. Many plants with two ears, flag leaves common. A few very short tillers. Long tassel branches closely arranged on branching portion of central spike. Secondary branches common and tertiary tassel branches somewhat infrequent.

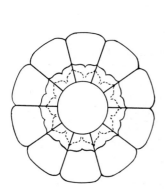

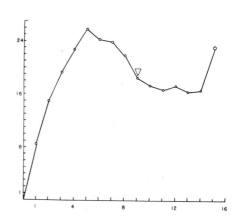

FIG. 69. Ear cross-section diagram of Argentino.

FIG. 70. Internode pattern of Argentino.

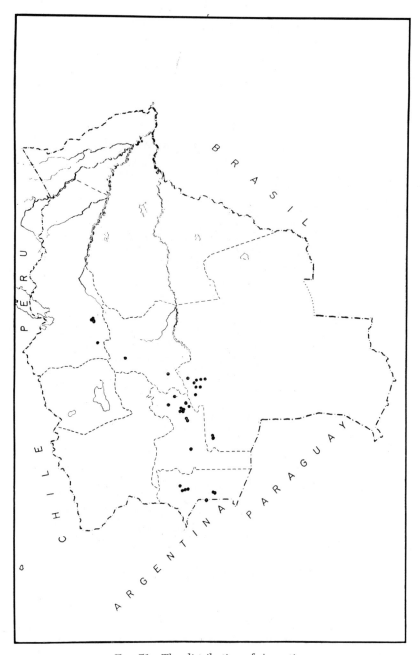

Fig. 71. The distribution of Argentino.

NIÑUELO

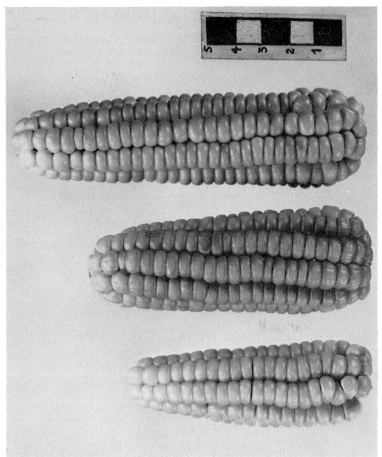

Fig. 72. Representative ears of the type specimens of Niñuelo.

Mean altitude of type specimens 1900 meters. Others 1800–2000 meters. Typical collections: Bov. 451, Bov. 495, Bov. 1088. Ears medium to small, 8-rowed, cylindrical to slightly tapering. Rounded white flint kernels. Little or no husk compression. White cobs. Longest ears more than three times as long as wide. Short slender stalk with comparatively long internodes. High frequency of medium intense sun red color. Leaves short and narrow with high degree of stiff pubescence on the sheaths. Two eared plants predominate with principal ear in about the middle of the plant. Flag leaves common. Practically no tillers. Extremely long tassel peduncle. Tassel branches of medium length, secondary branches common and relatively high frequency of tertiary tassel branches. Very little husk condensation at terminal end of ear shank.

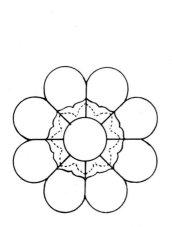

FIG. 73. Ear cross-section diagram of Niñuelo.

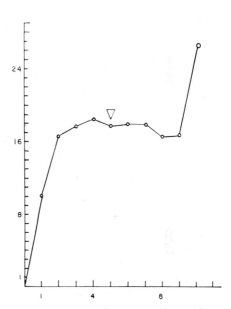

FIG. 74. Internode pattern of Niñuelo.

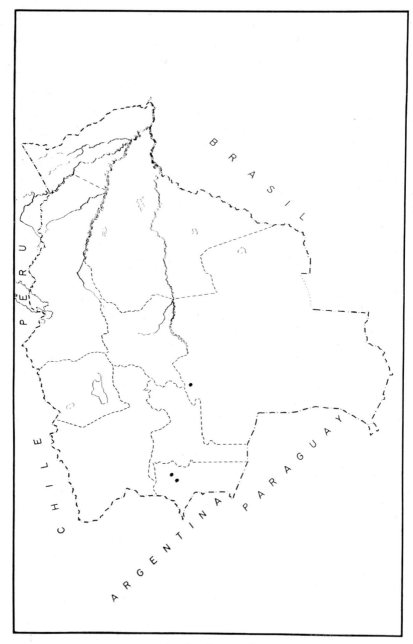

Fig. 75. The distribution of Niñuelo.

CAMBA

FIG. 76. Representative ears of the type specimens of Camba.

Mean altitude of type specimens 1350 meters. Others 360–2000 meters. Typical collections: Bov. 1131, Bov. 1133. Long ears with strong and regular tapering. 14 or more rows; kernels floury with deep smooth dent. White endosperm. Offtype kernels yellow and bronze. White cobs. Medium to large shanks. The name means "savage" or "forest man." Late maturing, thick stemmed, extremely tall plant with very long leaves which are proportionately narrow to their length. Internodes are deep sun red. Great amount of stiff pubescence on leaf sheaths. Tall tillers common. Numerous plants with two ears. Many long tassel branches. Exceptionally high frequency of secondary and tertiary tassel branches. Most plants exhibit flag leaves and adventitious roots. Extreme one-eared tendency.

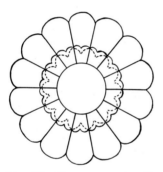

Fig. 77. Ear cross-section diagram of Camba.

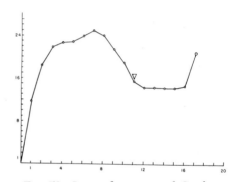

Fig. 78. Internode pattern of Camba.

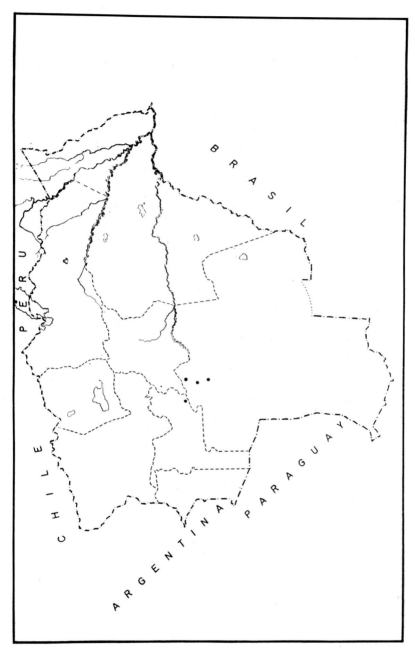

Fig. 79. The distribution of Camba.

MORADO

Ear Photographs,   Figure 80
Ear Diagram,   Figure 81
Internode Diagram, Figure 82
Distribution Map,   Figure 83

Fɪɢ. 80. Representative ears of the type specimens of Morado.

Mean altitude of type specimens 1592 meters. Others 130–2270 meters. Typical collections: Bov. 740, Bov. 786, Bov. 1126. This race is probably related to the *Coroicos*. All three collections were uniform both within and between groups. Ears medium long and slightly tapered; slightly irregular rowing; base of ear more or less knobby. 12 to 18 rows of small, non-pointed kernels. Floury endosperm. Cherry or red pericarp. Probably selected as a dye corn. Very tall plant, medium thick stalk with intense sun red plant color; deep purple plant color also very common. Leaf sheaths highly pubescent. Many tillering plants, most of which are tall. The tassels are somewhat dense, with many secondary and tertiary branches. Flag leaves and adventitious roots common when grown at Palmira.

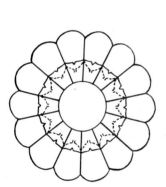

FIG. 81. Ear cross-section diagram of Morado.

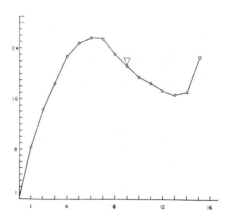

FIG. 82. Internode pattern of Morado.

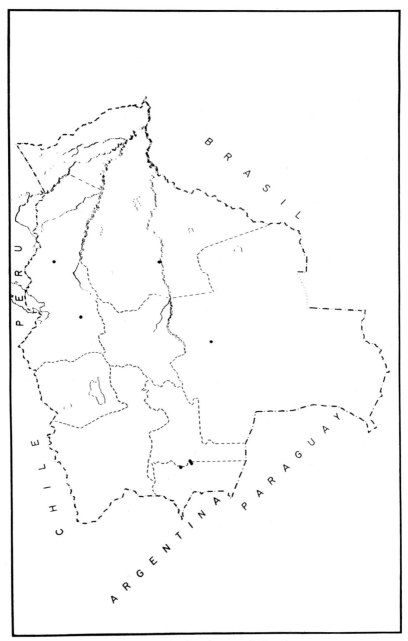

Fig. 83. The distribution of Morado.

PEROLA

Ear Photographs,   Figure 84
Ear Diagram,   Figure 85
Internode Diagram, Figure 86
Distribution Map,   Figure 87

Fig. 84. Representative ears of the type specimens of Perola.

Mean altitude of type specimens 805 meters. Others 140–2000 meters. Typical collections: Bov. 361, Bov. 711, Bov. 712. Ears, long, slender, cylindrical. White flinty endosperm; occasionally with slight capping. 12 to 14 rows of nearly round kernels. White cob. Medium small shank. This race, it seems, may be quite similar to one of the White Flint Synthetics from Bolivia described by Brieger, *et al* (8), and to which they have assigned the name "Cristal Perola." Plants of medium height with somewhat thick stalk, predominately green plant color with some light sun red. Tillers of medium height common. Strong degree of harsh pubescence. Internodes of increasing length in lower third of plant; upper two-thirds of plant has internodes of decreasing length. Many secondary tassel branches borne on a dense appearing tassel. Most plants have two silking ears and a number have three silking ears.

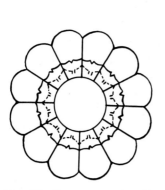

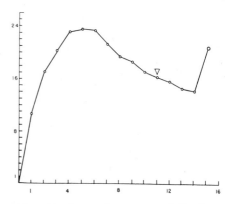

Fig. 85. Ear cross-section diagram of Perola.

Fig. 86. Internode pattern of Perola.

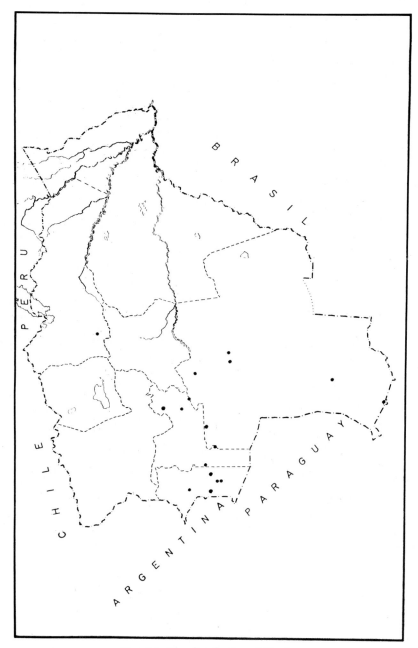

Fɪɢ. 87. The distribution of Perola.

YUNGUEÑO

Ear Photographs,   Figure 88
Ear Diagram,   Figure 89
Internode Diagram, Figure 90
Distribution Map,   Figure 91

Fig. 88. Representative ears of the type specimens of Yungueño.

Mean altitude of type specimens 1025 meters. Others 995–2720 meters. Typical collections: Bov. 665, Bov. 716, Bov. 747. Ears long, cylindrical to slightly tapering; 12 to 14 rowed; frequent multiplication; capping slight to strong; denting slight to strong. Kernels small to medium wide. Endosperm mostly yellow. Some purple and bronze aleurone. Large shanks. Cobs white and red. There is reason to believe that Yungueño may be related to Amageceno or Comun of Colombia. Somewhat long wide leaves on plant of medium height with round stem. Some tillering, strong sun red and purple plant color. Wiry pubescence. Tassels dense, many secondary branches. Husks at base of ear somewhat condensed. Flag leaves and adventitious roots common. Tendency of two silking ears very strong.

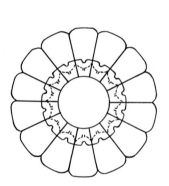

FIG. 89. Ear cross-section diagram of Yungueño.

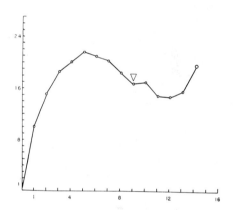

FIG. 90. Internode pattern of Yungueño.

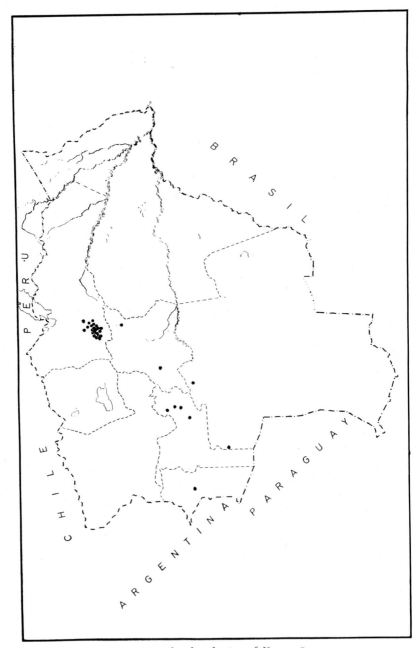

Fig. 91. The distribution of Yungueño.

POJOSO CHICO

Ear Photographs,   Figure 92
Ear Diagram,   Figure 93
Internode Diagram, Figure 94
Distribution Map, Figure 95

Fig. 92. Representative ears of the type specimens of Pojoso Chico.

Mean altitude of type specimens 925 meters. Others 80– 2300 meters. Typical collections: Bov. 755, Bov. 800, Bov. 809. This race is obviously related to Coroico but differs from the latter in having shorter ears, more rows of kernels and less interlocking of grains. Ears of medium length with strong taper, 12 to 18 rows; irregular at base. Tesselate kernel arrangement. Endosperm floury; kernels white to light yellow to bright yellow to bronze. Cobs white. Fairly short plant in comparison to the other lowland races. Slender stalk. Exceptionally long leaves which are proportionately narrow. Predominately green plant color with some degree of light sun red. Some tillers of varying height. Two silking ears on most plants. Very high frequency of flag leaves. Medium amount of pubescence, most of which is stiff.

FIG. 93. Ear cross-section diagram of Pojoso Chico.

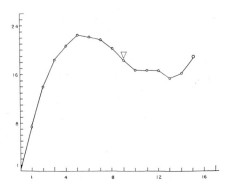

FIG. 94. Internode pattern of Pojoso Chico.

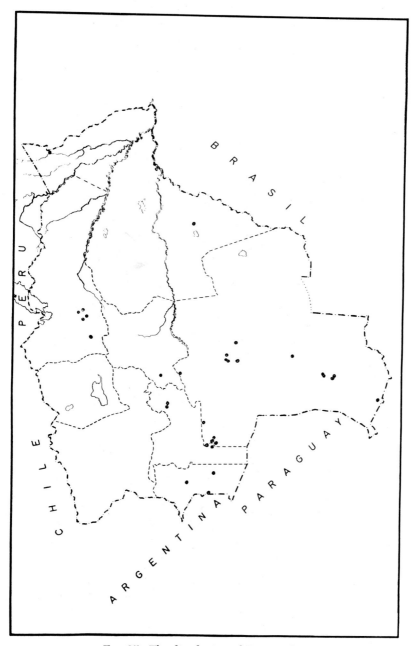

Fig. 95. The distribution of Pojoso Chico.

CHOLITO

Ear Photographs,   Figure 96
Ear Diagram,   Figure 97
Internode Diagram, Figure 98
Distribution Map,   Figure 99

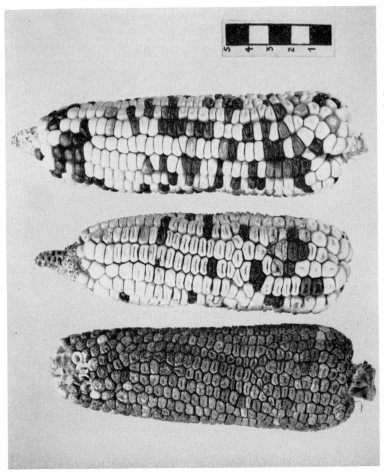

FIG. 96. Representative ears of the type specimens of Cholito.

Mean altitude of type specimens 800 meters. Others 500–1200 meters. Typical collections: Bov. 705, Bov. 707, Bov. 781. Cylindrical ears of medium length; 16 to 20 rows of tesselate kernels. Ears with rounded butts and strong husk compression. Endosperm floury with medium to deep dent. Purple or dotted aleurone mostly segregating white. White cob. Medium to large shank. Plant is fairly short with leaves of medium length and thickness when compared to other races grown at Palmira. Some purple plant color and light sun red but plants are, for the most part, green. Somewhat stiffly pubescent. Very few tillers, most of which are tall. Fairly short dense tassel, tassel branches long in comparison to tassel size, many secondary branches, a few tertiaries. Majority of plants have two silking ears. Incidence of flag leaves and superfluous prop roots very high.

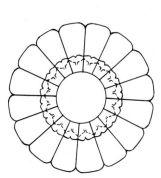

Fig. 97. Ear cross-section diagram of Cholito.

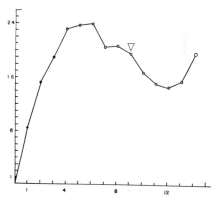

Fig. 98. Internode pattern of Cholito.

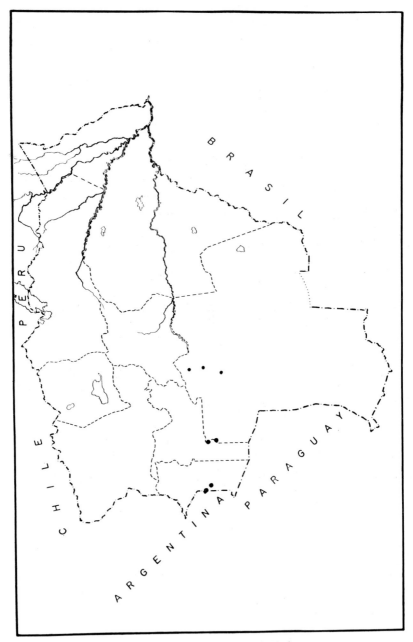

FIG. 99. The distribution of Cholito.

CUBANO DENTADO

FIG. 100. Representative ears of the type specimens of Cubano Dentado.

Mean altitude of type specimens 445 meters. Others 330–560 meters. Typical collections: Bov. 440, Bov. 585. Cubano Dentado, as the name implies, is very similar to the common yellow dents of the West Indian Islands. It has probably been introduced into Bolivia as a commercial corn. Ears are of medium length and cylindrical with 12 to 16 rows of strongly capped to slightly dented yellow kernels. Shanks are of medium diameter. Cobs white. Plant of medium height, fairly wide leaves of medium length. Early maturity, highly resistant or tolerant to rust and *Helminthosporium* at Palmira. High incidence of wiry pubescence. Medium intensity of sun red plant color. Slight amount of tillering. Plants predominately two-eared with strong husk condensation at terminal end of shank. Short branching portion of tassel with considerably fewer tassel branches than most of the lowland material. Relatively few secondary branches.

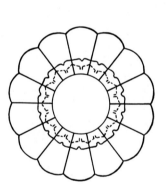

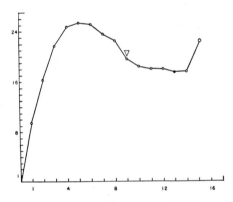

Fig. 101. Ear cross-section diagram of Cubano Dentado.

Fig. 102. Internode pattern of Cubano Dentado.

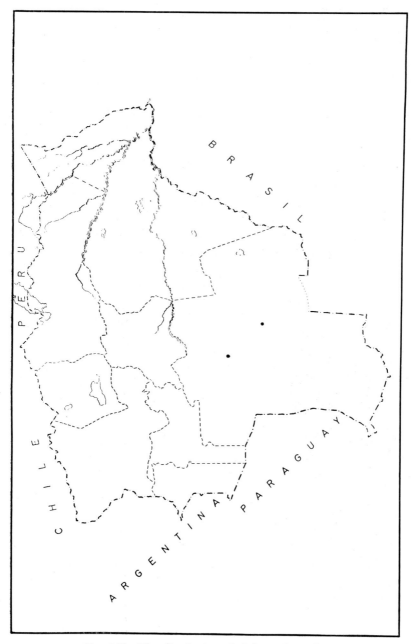

Fig. 103. The distribution of Cubano Dentado.

CATETO

Fig. 104. Representative ears of the type specimens of Cateto.

Mean altitude of type specimens 240 meters. Others 140–2000 meters. Typical collections: Bov. 635, Bov. 815, Bov. 1083. Ears are medium long, slender with rounded butts. 14 rows of deep orange, flinty to slightly capped kernels. Kernels rounded at the top and tightly packed. Medium to wide shanks. White cob. Plants very tall with dark green arching leaves. Stem predominately green with few sun red and fewer purple. Very long culm internodes, usually well exserted. Tassels slightly drooping to stiff upright. No tillers. Fairly high frequency of two ears. Numerous primary tassel branches.

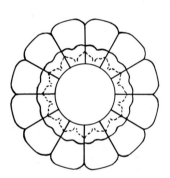

Fig. 105. Ear cross-section diagram of Cateto.

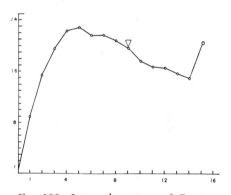

Fig. 106. Internode pattern of Cateto.

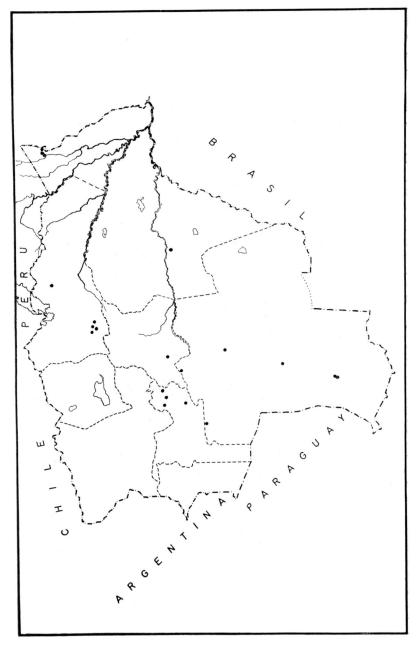

Fig. 107. The distribution of Cateto.

PORORO

Fig. 108. Representative ears of the type specimens of Pororo.

Mean altitude of type specimens 330 meters. Typical collections: Bov. 583, Bov. 587, Bov. 806. Medium small ears; cylindrical to very slight taper. Small flinty kernels, rounded or very slightly pointed at micropyle. 16 to 18 rows. Pericarp red or colorless. Some yellow endosperm. Cob white or red. Shank small but adherent. Resembling Pira of Colombia in some respects. Short plant, slender stalk with short narrow leaves. Very intense sun red plant color. Appreciable amount of medium soft pilosity. Extremely high frequency of tillers, the majority being tall. Short dense tassel with a long central spike. Relatively few secondary or tertiary tassel branches. Most plants have two silking ears. Slight incidence of flag leaves. No adventitious roots.

Fig. 109. Ear cross-section diagram of Pororo.

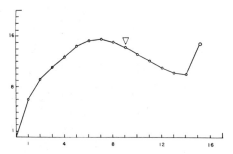

Fig. 110. Internode pattern of Pororo.

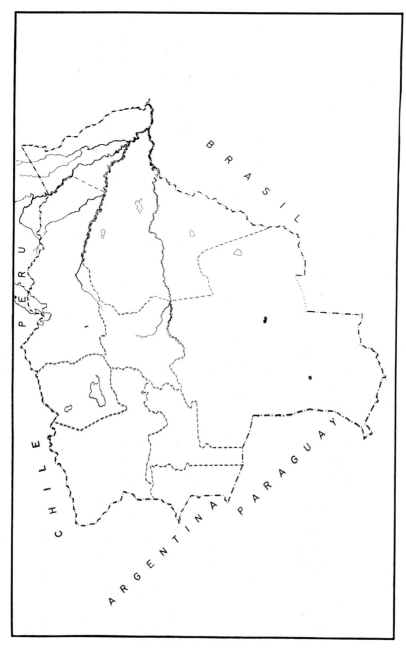

Fig. 111. The distribution of Pororo.

COROICO BLANCO

Fɪɢ. 112. Representative ears of the type specimens of Coroico Blanco.

Mean altitude of type specimens 150 meters. Typical collections: Bov. 1034, Bov. 1045, Bov. 1048. Ears long and gently tapered. Approximately 18 poorly defined rows of tesselate kernels. Some multiplication. Kernels mostly flinty but with some soft starch. Large adherent, irregular shanks. Aleurone mostly colorless. White cobs. General plant aspect similar to that of Coroico. Drooping leaves. Plants tall with ears placed high. Numerous plants with two ears. Tassels large and mostly exserted with lax, arching branches. Tassel green and purple. Purple anthers common. Stem medium stout with well exserted internodes and with slight tendency to zigzag. Sheaths harshly pubescent. Stem color varies from green through sun red to purple. Purple ends of exserted internodes striking. No tillers.

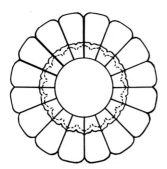

Fig. 113. Ear cross-section diagram of Coroico Blanco.

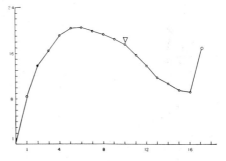

Fig. 114. Internode pattern of Coroico Blanco.

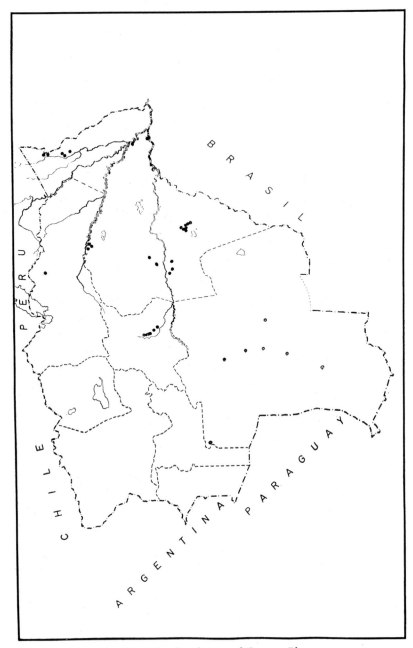

Fig. 115. The distribution of Coroico Blanco.

COROICO AMARILLO

Ear Photographs,   Figure 116
Ear Diagram,   Figure 117
Internode Diagram, Figure 118
Distribution Map, Figure 119

Fɪɢ. 116. Representative ears of the type specimens of Coroico Amarillo.

Mean altitude of type specimens 166 meters. Others 80–1000 meters. Typical collections: Bov. 405, Bov. 1000, Bov. 1077. Ears long with enlarged butts and strongly tapered. 12 to 14 rows of interlocked grains. Endosperm floury. White cobs. Plants similar in appearance to Coroico but somewhat later in maturity. Leaves lax and drooping. Stem slender, ranging in color from green to sun red to purple. Ears placed high on plant. Tassels with long, drooping branches. Plants somewhat less robust than Coroico.

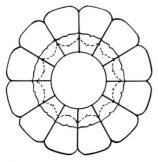

Fig. 117. Ear cross-section diagram of Coroico Amarillo.

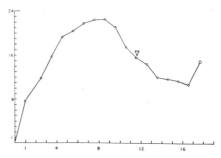

Fig. 118. Internode pattern of Coroico Amarillo.

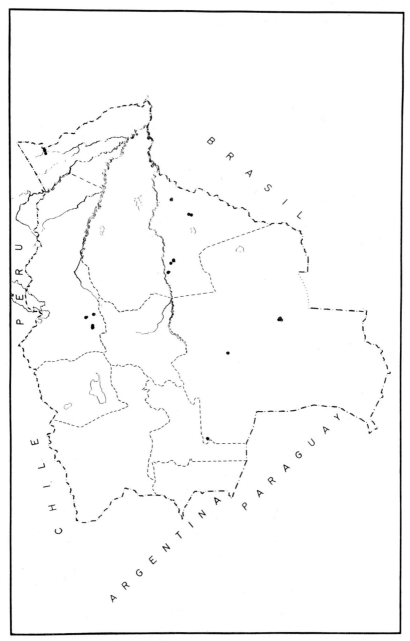

Fig. 119. The distribution of Coroico Amarillo.

COROICO

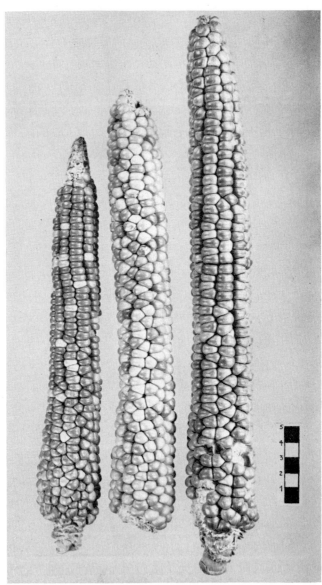

Fɪɢ. 120. Representative ears of the type specimens of Coroico.

Mean altitude of type specimens 190 meters. Others 100–1390 meters. Typical collections: Bov. 992, Bov. 1035, Bov. 1063. Ears dull grayish orange; aleurone orange-red over white endosperm; pericarp segregating orange and different intensities of orange red. Ears very long and tapering with pronounced butt. Kernels interlocked. Considerable multiplication. Row number approximately 10. Rowing very irregular and difficult to estimate. Cobs white or red. Shanks large, adherent and irregular. Tassels many branched, varying from lax to slightly upright. Most tassels well exserted at maturity. Leaves proportionately narrow for height of plant. Internodes variable, some exserted. Tillers, none to few, when grown at Palmira. Many plants with two ears. Ears placed high on plant. Leaves light to medium green. Stem color variable from green to sun red. Stems slender. This is one of the most unusual races of maize in Bolivia. It was first described by Cutler (*15*) and named for the town of Coroico, near which it was first collected. Later, a number of races and sub-races of Coroico were described by Brieger, *et al* (*8*) and given the name of "Interlocked Flour Corn" because of the unusual arrangement of the alicoles resulting in interlocked grain.

FIG. 121. Ear cross-section diagram of Coroico.

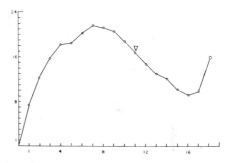

FIG. 122. Internode pattern of Coroico.

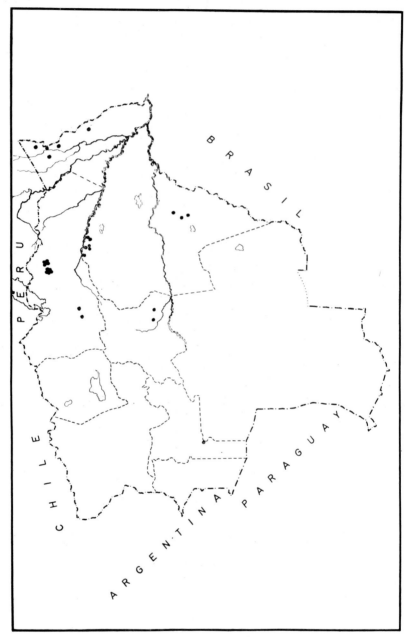

Fig. 123. The distribution of Coroico,

ENANO

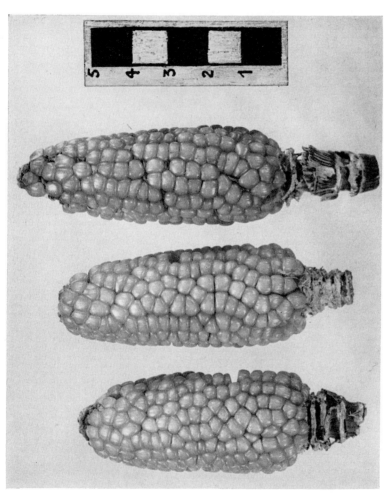

FIG. 124. Representative ears of the type specimens of Enano.

Mean altitude of type specimens 170 meters. Others 170–220 meters. Typical collections: Bov. 1036, Bov. 1043. Ears are very small and slightly conical with 16 to 18 rows of tiny, flinty kernels. Kernels ivory white in color, tesselate, and tightly compacted on the cob. Much multiplication. Some cupules with extra kernels. Aleurone colorless. Cobs white. Shank large, adherent and highly indurated. Many highly condensed internodes at juncture of shank and cob. Plants short, without tillers and with fairly upright leaves. Sun red color common on both sheaths and culm, also some purple stems. Leaves extremely hard and brittle. Tassels small with relatively few primary branches which may be whorled at the lower nodes. Tassels upright, more or less "whisk broom" in appearance. Tassel exsertion variable, from inserted to well exserted. Glumes usually sun red. Ear upright with extremely tight and brittle husks. Shank very hard even when green. Stem has slight tendency to zigzag. Stem very thick, with hard rind. Enano is of early maturity and is one of the most interesting races in Bolivia. Although it is grown in the same general region as Coroico, it apparently has not appeared in earlier collections.

Fig. 125. Ear cross-section diagram of Enano.

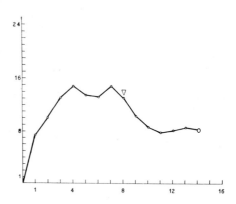

Fig. 126. Internode pattern of Enano.

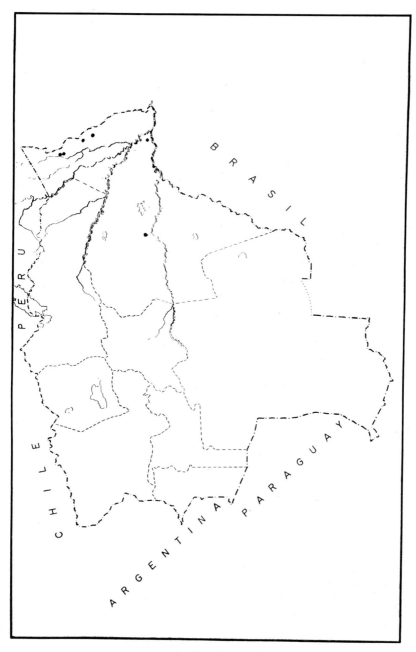

Fɪɢ. 127. The distribution of Enano.

SUMMARY

1. This report is based on a detailed study of 844 collections of
    Bolivian maize. Among the collections, thirty-two (32) more or
    less distinct races are recognized. The classification into
    racial entities was made first on the basis of ear characteristics
    and geographical distribution of the original collections. This
    tentative classification was further checked by a careful study
    of plant, ear and other characteristics of progenies of the
    original collections grown at two or more locations.

2. General descriptions, tabular data on ears, plants, tassels, etc.
    internode diagrams, ear cross sectional diagrams, distribution
    maps and ear photographs are presented for each race. In
    contrast to previous publications in this series, little attention
    is given to the origin and relationships of Bolivian races. In-
    formation of this nature will need to await results from in-
    breeding and crossing.

3. A brief resume is given of the geography of Bolivia, its maize
    growing regions, its indigenous peoples and the varied uses
    they make of maize.

4. Positions as well as numbers of chromosome knobs were de-
    termined for eighteen of the thirty-two races described. With
    one exception (Pisankalla) the Andean races of Bolivian maize
    are an extremely homogenous group in so far as their knob
    constitution is concerned. Each of these races carried a
    medium to small knob in the long arm of chromosome 7. The
    only other knob present is at the lower position in the long
    arm of chromosome 6. This knob occurred in 44 of the 56
    plants examined. Knob patterns of races from lower elevations
    are much more variable than those from the highlands. Cer-
    tain of these possess the typical "Andean" knobs in addition
    to others from unknown sources. B type chromosomes were
    found to be more prevalent among the highland races than
    from intermediate and lower altitudes.

5. The collections of Bolivian maize are of value for several
    reasons. In the first place certain collections now in storage
    are irreplaceable. Secondly, an understanding of local varieties
    is an essential prerequisite to maize improvement in ancient
    centers of maize variability such as Bolivia. Finally, it is sug-

gested that in experiments designed to shed light on the problems of heterosis, certain Bolivian races whose evolutionary histories differ drastically from that of the common maize of the United States cornbelt may provide critical material for experiments in this field of investigation.

LITERATURE CITED

1. Acosta, José de. 1940. Historia Natural y Moral de las Indias, Mexico.
2. Balcazar, Juan Manuel. 1956. Historia de la Medicina en Bolivia, La Paz.
3. ————. 1948. A reappraisal of Peruvian archeology, Amer. Antiquity, Vol. XIII, No. 4, Part 2.
4. Bird, Junius. 1938. Antiquity and migrations of the early inhabitants of Patagonia, Geog. Rev. Vol. 28, 250–273.
5. ————. 1946. The archeology of Patagonia in handbook of South American Indians, Vol. 1. (Steward, Ed.)
6. ————. 1948. America's oldest farmers, Natural History, Vol. 57, No. 7, 296–303, 334–335.
7. Bowman, Isaiah. 1916. The Andes of Southern Peru, New York.
8. Brieger, F. G., Gurgel, J. T. A., Paterniani, E., Blumenschein, A., and Alleoni, M. R. 1958. Races of maize in Brazil and other Eastern South American Countries. Nat. Acad. Sci. — Nat. Res. Council Pub. No. 593.
9. Brown, William L. 1949. Numbers and distribution of chromosome knobs in United States maize. Genetics, Vol. 34, 524–536.
10. Cardenas, Martin. 1945. Aspecto general de la vegetacion de Bolivia. In Plants and Plant Science in Latin America, Chron. Bot., Vol. 16, 312–313.
11. ————. 1945. Recursos generales del reino vegetal en Bolivia. In Plants and Plant Science in Latin America, Chron. Bot., Vol. 16, 313–315.
12. ————. 1950. Plantas alimenticias nativas de Bolivia, Folia Universetaria, Nos. 2, 3, 4. Universidad de Cochabamba.
13. ———— and Cutler, H. C. 1947. Chicha, a native South American beer, Bot. Mus. Leaf., Vol. 13, No. 3. Harvard Univ.
14. Cobo, Bernabé. 1890–5. Historia del Nuevo Mundo. Seville.
15. Cutler, H. C. 1946. Races of Maize in South America. Bot. Mus. Leaflets, Harvard Univ., Vol. 12: 257–291.
16. Dion, H. G. 1950. Agriculture in the Altiplano of Bolivia, F.A.O. Development Paper, No. 4. Washington.
17. Direccion General de Meteorologia. 1957. Annuario Metereologico, La Paz, Bolivia.
18. Direccion Nacional de Estadistica y Censos. 1950. Censo Agropecuario, La Paz, Bolivia.
19. Garcilaso de la Vega. 1943. Comentarios Reales de los Incas, Buenos Aires.
20. ————. 1943. Historia general del Peru. Segunda parte de los Comentarios, Reales de los Incas, Buenos Aires.
21. Hohenthal, W. D. 1951. The concept of cultural marginality and native agriculture in South America, Thesis (PH.D), Univ. of California, Berkeley.
22. Latchman, Richardo, E. 1936. La agricultura precolombina en Chile y los Paises Vecinos, Ediciones de la Universidad de Chile.
23. Leonard, Olen. 1952. Bolivia: Land, people and institutions, Washington.
24. Longley, A. E. 1938. Chromosomes of maize from North American Indians. Jour. Agr. Res. Vol. 56: 177–195.

25. Lévi-Strauss, Claude. 1948. Tribes of the Right Bank of the Guaporé River, In Handbook of South American Indians, Vol. 3 (Steward, Ed.)

26. Mangelsdorf, P. C. and Reeves, R. G. 1939. The origin of Indian corn and its relatives. Texas Agr. Exp. Sta. Bul. 574.

27. Mason, J. Alden. 1957. The ancient civilizations of Peru, Pelican Books.

28. Means, Phillip A. 1931. Ancient civilizations of the Andes, New York.

29. Mercado Encinas, Miguel. 1956. Esto es Bolivia: Geographia general de Bolivia Ed. Universo, La Paz.

30. Mesa Bernal, Daniel. 1957. Historia natural del Maiz. Rev. de la Arcad. Colomb. de Cienc. Exact. Fis. y Nat., Vol. X, No. 39: 13–106.

31. Métraux, Alfred. 1942. The native tribes of Eastern Bolivia and Western Mato Grasso, In Bull. 134 Smithsonian Inst. Bur. of Am. Eth., Washington, D. C.

32. ———. 1946. Ethnography of the Chaco in Handbook of South American Indians, Vol. 1. (Steward, Ed.).

33. ———. 1948. Tribes of Eastern Bolivia and the Maderia Headwaters, In Handbook of South American Indians, Vol. 3, (Steward, Ed.).

34. ———. 1948. The Paressi (the tribes of Mato Grosso and Eastern Bolivia) In Handbook of South American Indians, Vol. 3, (Steward, Ed.).

35. ———. 1948. Tribes of the Eastern Slopes of the Bolivian Andes In Handbook of South American Indians, Vol. 3, (Steward, Ed.).

36. Nordenskiöld, Erland. 1924. The ethnography of South America seen from Mojos in Bolivia, Comparative Ethnographical Studies, Vol. 3, Göteborg.

37. ———. 1931. Origin of the Indian civilization in South America, Comparative Ethno. Studies, Vol. 9, Göteborg.

38. ———. 1904–05. Investigaciones Arquelogicas en la region fronteriza de Peru y Bolivia. Trad. de Carlos Ponce Sanginés y Stig Rydén, Alcaldia Municipal, Biblioteca Pacenta, La Paz. 1953.

39. Ogilvie, Alan G. 1922. Geography of the Central Andes, Amer. Geo. Soc. Pub. No. 1.

40. Orbiguy, Alcides. 1839. El Hombre Americano, Trans. from the French original. Ed. Futuro, B.A., 1944.

41. Osborn, Harold. 1952. Indians of the Andes, London.

42. ———. 1955. Bolivia. Royal Inst. of Int. Aff., London (2nd Ed.).

43. Otero, Gustavo Adolfo. 1951. La Piedra Magica. Instituto Indeginista Interamericano, Mexico.

44. Pando Gutierrez, Jorge. 1947. Bolivia y el Mundo, La Paz.

45. Parodi, Lorenzo, R. 1935. Relaciones de la agricultura prehispanica en la agricultura Argentina actual, An. Acad. Nac. Agron. Vet., Vol. 1: 115–167.

46. Peña y Lillo Escobar, Abel. 1947. Simtesis geografica de Bolivia, La Paz.

47. Posnansky, Arthur. 1938. Antorpologia y sociologia de los Razas Interandinas, Instituto Tihuanacu de Antropologia, Etnografia y Prehistoria, La Paz, Bolivia.

48. ———. 1945 and 1947. Tihuanacu: La cuna del hombre Americano (Bilingual), (4 Vols.), Minesterio de Educacion, La Paz.

49. Prada, E. Roberto. 1946. Climas de Bolivia, La Paz.

50. Radin, P. 1946. Indians of South America, New York.

51. Renner, O. 1925. Untersuchungen über die faktorielle Konstitution einiger komplexheterozygotischen Oenotheren. Bibliotheca Genetica 9.

52. Reeves, R. G. 1944. Chromosome knobs in relation to the origin of maize. Genetics Vol. 29: 141–147.

53. Roberts, L. M., Grant, U. J., Ramírez E., Ricardo, Hatheway, W. H. and Smith, D. L. in collaboration with Mangelsdorf, Paul C. 1957. Races of Maize in Colombia. Nat. Acad. Sci. — Nat. Res. Council Pub. No. 510.

APPENDIX

TABLE 6. Races of Maize of Bolivia Compared in Characters of the Plants

Race	Adaptation to Altitude (meters)	Height (cm.)		Stem Diameter (mm.)		Leaves			Ears per plant	Tillers			
		Plants	Ears	Minimum	Maximum	Length (cm.)	Width (cm.)	Venation index		Number	Tall	Med.	Short
												Height %	
Confite Puneño	3730	43.1	19.8	12.5	15.2	30.7	2.2	4.06	1.0	0.00	—	—	—
Altiplano	2980	107.3	58.1	18.0	20.0	60.2	7.4	2.47	1.6	0.03	—	—	100
Patillo	3280	60.4	31.3	14.3	16.1	37.3	4.7	2.93	1.0	0.00	—	—	—
Kcello	3560	89.2	42.1	16.3	18.4	47.1	5.7	2.68	1.3	0.00	—	—	—
Kulli	3420	85.0	48.8	18.9	21.1	55.3	7.0	2.49	1.6	0.00	—	—	—
Huilcaparu	2680	162.3	108.3	23.1	26.1	71.4	11.1	2.34	2.0	0.10	50	50	0.0
Chake-Sara	2410	115.0	73.8	19.1	20.8	67.5	9.2	2.11	1.7	0.00	—	—	—
Aysuma	2890	91.7	39.9	16.1	17.8	42.6	5.4	2.82	1.2	0.00	—	—	—
Patillo Grande	2320	117.3	65.7	21.4	24.2	68.1	8.2	2.43	1.6	0.13	0.0	50	50
Checchi	2520	93.7	50.8	19.1	21.5	49.7	6.1	2.83	1.3	0.00	—	—	—
Cuzco-Huilcaparu	2340	143.8	71.0	19.2	22.2	63.7	8.2	2.59	1.6	0.00	—	—	—
Paru	2800	115.3	64.5	18.4	20.4	65.0	8.0	2.54	1.4	0.00	—	—	—
Chuspillu	2490	135.7	93.1	19.2	21.5	68.3	9.2	2.56	2.0	0.03	100	—	—
Cuzco Boliviano	2650	132.0	83.4	17.5	19.6	72.5	7.9	2.63	1.2	0.00	—	—	—
Pisankalla	2240	90.8	60.3	14.8	13.8	63.0	6.4	2.59	1.5	0.67	42	44	14
Uchuquilla	2160	119.3	76.6	19.5	21.7	67.0	7.7	2.31	1.7	0.13	0.0	50	50
Karapampa	2120	102.7	61.6	17.4	19.0	57.5	8.1	2.14	1.4	0.09	0.0	0.0	100
Argentino	1570	290.2	198.6	28.7	30.5	107.0	11.4	2.52	1.4	0.23	0.0	16	84
Niñuelo	1900	188.0	95.6	21.8	23.2	77.2	7.5	2.61	1.5	0.03	0.0	0.0	100
Camba	1380	308.5	235.8	29.2	30.2	125.1	10.5	2.62	1.1	0.69	48	0.0	52
Morado	1590	280.3	181.5	26.7	27.8	105.6	10.4	2.48	1.6	0.55	55	7	38
Perola	800	269.3	188.4	27.6	29.5	104.5	10.9	2.58	2.0	0.76	44	45	11
Yunqueño	1020	260.3	166.5	27.0	28.7	108.8	11.0	2.43	1.7	0.22	56	22	22
Pojoso Chico	920	234.7	159.0	24.0	25.6	134.9	10.1	2.59	1.8	0.43	40	58	2
Cholito	800	231.0	146.1	26.2	27.6	100.8	10.4	2.52	1.9	0.12	43	26	21
Cubano Dentado	440	288.0	184.7	27.5	29.4	106.6	11.5	2.60	1.6	0.18	0	75	25
Cateto	240	260.3	180.0	27.3	29.3	100.9	11.5	2.46	1.8	0.29	67	33	0
Pororo	330	175.0	115.8	21.8	23.8	84.4	8.6	2.89	1.7	2.50	86	4	10
Coroico Blanco	170	250.0	171.9	26.6	27.7	108.0	10.9	2.55	1.7	0.40	34	42	24
Coroico Amarillo	150	221.0	143.6	25.5	26.9	103.9	10.6	2.45	1.4	0.83	38	24	38
Coroico	180	258.0	190.9	29.5	30.3	109.2	11.0	2.65	1.6	0.33	57	26	17
Enano	170	161.0	116.6	18.2	20.6	88.9	8.2	2.36	1.6	0.00	—	—	—

TABLE 7. Races of Maize of Bolivia Compared in Characters of the Tassels.

Race	Length (cm.)				Best Developed Primary Branch			Number of Primary Branches		
	Peduncle	Branching Portion	Central Spike	Uppermost Primary Branch	Length (cm.)	Number of Secondaries	Number of Tertiaries	Total	with Secondaries	with Tertiaries
Confite Puneño	15.2	2.7	12.6	5.6	7.2	0.02	0.00	2.6	0.17	0.00
Altiplano	16.7	10.6	20.8	12.5	19.9	1.30	0.00	12.0	3.17	0.03
Patillo	16.9	5.3	13.0	8.2	11.5	0.16	0.00	6.4	0.48	0.00
Kcello	16.4	7.6	18.5	12.0	17.4	0.61	0.00	7.8	3.50	0.00
Kulli	17.8	8.8	19.3	12.5	17.2	0.72	0.00	10.4	1.62	0.00
Huilcaparu	14.1	12.3	17.3	11.5	18.4	1.70	0.07	15.7	7.16	0.20
Chake-Sara	17.5	11.4	24.3	12.8	20.7	1.33	0.00	14.0	3.76	0.00
Aysuma	18.3	6.4	17.1	10.6	15.1	0.47	0.00	8.4	1.53	0.00
Patillo Grande	20.0	11.4	24.7	14.7	23.1	1.03	0.00	13.4	2.80	0.03
Checchi	19.8	9.1	20.4	13.1	18.9	0.96	0.03	10.8	1.86	0.03
Cuzco-Huilcaparu	17.5	11.4	20.9	13.4	20.4	1.43	0.17	12.8	3.75	0.18
Paru	16.6	10.8	19.5	12.1	19.8	1.17	0.00	14.7	3.20	0.00
Chuspillu	15.1	11.2	17.3	10.3	14.0	1.60	0.04	19.6	6.18	0.11
Cuzco Boliviano	18.6	12.7	20.1	13.0	22.0	1.52	0.00	11.7	4.36	0.06
Pisankalla	20.4	6.2	24.9	13.8	18.4	0.83	0.00	8.5	0.80	0.00
Uchuquilla	18.5	12.6	23.3	15.2	23.1	1.33	0.00	12.3	3.93	0.00
Karapampa	16.0	9.3	20.7	12.9	18.7	2.97	0.00	3.8	1.96	0.00
Argentino	23.0	20.9	19.9	16.4	26.8	2.56	0.33	22.7	7.77	0.47
Niñuelo	26.3	16.9	23.0	16.2	25.0	2.03	2.73	11.3	3.33	0.27
Camba	20.7	21.2	22.6	17.5	26.8	3.68	1.12	29.7	12.00	2.07
Morado	22.3	22.3	22.3	15.5	26.4	3.30	0.97	26.2	9.90	1.10
Perola	20.6	19.5	20.7	15.6	25.3	2.66	0.36	23.9	7.96	0.70
Yunqueño	19.3	17.3	19.8	16.3	25.9	2.57	0.48	27.0	7.97	0.82
Pojoso Chico	20.0	18.6	17.9	14.1	24.8	2.90	0.43	26.4	9.53	0.70
Cholito	19.4	17.7	19.7	17.1	23.4	2.57	0.40	26.4	8.67	0.60
Cubano Dentado	22.1	17.6	21.6	15.9	25.8	2.45	0.26	20.2	5.35	0.33
Cateto	20.3	18.1	16.6	14.9	26.0	2.43	0.33	23.0	6.86	0.47
Pororo	14.7	14.7	17.4	13.2	20.8	1.60	0.35	26.7	5.00	0.06
Coroico Blanco	16.6	20.6	20.7	16.3	26.8	3.13	0.70	33.6	9.80	1.10
Coroico Amarillo	14.6	18.4	17.1	14.8	23.3	2.43	0.26	30.8	9.37	0.57
Coroico	16.3	20.6	19.0	16.6	25.5	2.50	0.33	28.1	10.00	0.80
Enano	8.3	10.6	16.5	11.2	15.6	1.65	0.15	23.5	4.25	0.20

TABLE 8. Races of Maize of Bolivia Compared in External Characters of the Ears and Kernels.

Race	Row No.	Ears Length (cm.)	Diameter (mm.) Basal	Diameter (mm.) Mid-Point	Diameter (mm.) Tip	Number of Husks Total	Number of Husks Condensed	Kernels Length (mm.)	Kernels Width (mm.)	Kernels Thickness (mm.)	Kernels Hardness	Kernels Denting
Confite Puneño	14.0	5.8	34.2	34.4	26.9	5.1	3.0	9.72	6.65	5.27	3.5	5.0
Altiplano	12.2	8.6	40.6	41.8	33.4	7.2	3.4	13.09	7.97	5.08	4.6	4.3
Patillo	14.0	7.5	39.3	37.3	31.6	5.7	3.3	11.13	7.24	4.83	1.9	5.0
Kcello	10.0	11.9	37.2	36.6	26.9	6.5	3.4	12.89	9.52	4.14	3.0	4.8
Kulli	12.3	9.2	43.9	44.0	32.4	8.3	4.0	13.47	8.43	5.02	4.9	4.7
Huilcaparu	12.2	15.7	52.7	48.2	35.0	8.8	4.1	16.30	9.92	4.35	4.2	3.8
Chake-Sara	11.4	12.5	37.7	36.6	11.4	4.8	1.9	12.22	8.53	4.06	2.9	5.0
Aysuma	9.5	10.8	37.8	36.1	26.9	6.7	3.5	12.25	8.74	4.36	3.5	4.8
Patillo Grande	12.6	14.2	45.5	42.6	32.5	8.5	4.2	14.09	9.06	4.23	2.6	4.6
Checchi	13.5	10.6	44.7	43.2	32.2	7.3	3.4	13.54	9.03	4.24	5.0	4.1
Cuzco-Huilcaparu	9.2	12.2	45.3	48.1	33.7	7.9	3.2	14.60	10.67	4.53	4.1	4.1
Paru	18.1	9.8	57.8	57.1	41.6	7.6	3.2	17.41	7.58	5.02	5.0	3.9
Chuspillu	19.7	11.7	49.7	50.5	38.4	7.1	3.3	14.86	6.84	3.79	1.1	1.8
Cuzco Boliviano	8.7	14.4	53.4	52.9	38.8	8.1	3.6	18.30	13.40	5.06	4.7	4.1
Pisankalla	16.5	12.1	35.4	32.8	25.0	7.0	3.2	8.85	5.41	3.70	1.0	5.0
Uchuquilla	8.6	15.0	37.7	35.8	29.4	7.8	3.2	12.68	10.62	3.87	2.2	4.8
Karapampa	8.8	12.2	27.1	29.6	21.0	7.4	3.7	10.08	7.86	3.32	1.6	5.0
Argentino	10.4	17.9	44.5	42.9	36.2	12.7	5.5	12.23	8.89	4.24	2.5	2.8
Niñuelo	8.2	12.1	33.9	32.1	25.0	9.6	3.3	11.41	9.49	4.33	2.0	4.9
Camba	14.5	18.1	41.4	40.7	35.8	12.9	4.8	11.76	8.79	5.10	4.6	2.3
Morado	13.5	16.6	38.8	35.2	27.8	13.4	5.8	9.62	7.73	4.80	3.3	4.8
Perola	12.9	16.0	37.2	34.2	27.4	13.4	6.2	9.77	8.04	4.28	1.2	5.0
Yunqueño	13.4	18.4	36.9	43.3	33.5	14.2	6.7	12.40	9.07	4.54	2.6	4.2
Pojoso Chico	14.2	15.0	43.0	39.3	30.1	13.5	6.4	9.83	7.00	4.69	4.5	4.7
Cholito	16.2	13.5	42.5	41.9	33.7	11.6	5.2	11.56	7.70	4.15	4.9	2.9
Cubano Dentado	13.3	15.6	48.2	45.4	39.6	16.0	8.5	11.89	9.28	4.21	1.7	4.5
Cateto	12.9	17.0	38.6	35.4	29.9	14.0	6.8	9.59	8.12	4.17	1.3	5.0
Pororo	15.0	12.3	26.6	26.6	20.3	12.2	5.2	7.51	5.00	3.34	1.0	5.0
Coroico Blanco	16.4	20.3	46.4	39.2	29.9	17.6	9.5	9.56	7.69	4.91	2.8	5.0
Coroico Amarillo	12.9	23.1	42.8	37.9	29.8	15.5	8.4	9.70	8.88	5.48	4.5	5.0
Coroico	11.2	26.4	43.6	37.3	29.6	18.6	11.6	10.18	9.67	5.48	4.7	5.0
Enano	16.4	6.9	28.4	27.3	21.6	13.4	8.1	7.19	4.79	3.30	1.5	5.0

TABLE 9. Races of Maize of Bolivia Compared in Internal Characters of the Ears.

Race	Diameter (mm.)			Indices		Pubescence			Induration	
	Ear	Cob	Rachis	Cob/rachis	Glume/kernel	Cupule	Lower glume	Upper glume	Lower glume	Rachis
Confite Puneño	34.4	20.3	12.0	1.69	.43	1.2	0.8	0.5	1.0	1.1
Altiplano	41.8	22.4	13.4	1.67	.34	1.2	0.8	0.8	1.3	1.5
Patillo	37.3	22.3	12.9	1.73	.42	1.2	0.6	0.8	0.8	1.0
Kcello	36.6	18.1	10.3	1.76	.30	1.0	0.8	0.9	1.0	1.4
Kulli	44.0	21.1	14.1	1.50	.26	1.6	1.0	1.6	0.5	0.6
Huilcaparu	48.2	23.4	14.5	1.61	.27	1.0	1.1	1.3	1.7	1.9
Chake-Sara	36.6	18.3	10.6	1.73	.32	1.0	0.6	0.4	1.5	1.8
Aysuma	36.1	17.1	10.7	1.60	.26	1.2	1.0	0.7	1.4	1.5
Patillo Grande	42.6	21.5	13.1	1.64	.30	1.0	0.8	1.2	1.5	1.3
Checchi	43.2	20.5	13.2	1.55	.27	0.8	0.2	0.3	1.5	2.0
Cuzco-Huilcaparu	48.1	19.1	11.9	1.60	.25	1.0	1.0	0.6	1.4	1.9
Paru	57.1	25.1	15.8	1.59	.27	0.8	0.8	0.8	0.8	0.7
Chuspillu	50.5	25.8	17.3	1.49	.28	0.5	0.2	0.7	0.7	1.7
Cuzco Boliviano	52.9	23.8	14.3	1.66	.26	0.8	0.7	1.3	1.5	1.7
Pisankalla	32.8	21.6	12.4	1.74	.52	0.5	0.5	0.2	1.5	2.3
Uchuquilla	35.8	15.7	10.1	1.55	.22	0.3	0.0	0.2	0.3	2.0
Karapampa	29.6	12.7	6.7	1.90	.27	0.8	0.7	0.3	0.0	2.0
Argentino	42.9	23.1	15.0	1.54	.33	1.5	0.5	0.3	1.0	2.0
Niñuelo	32.1	14.2	8.5	1.67	.25	1.0	0.2	0.2	0.0	2.0
Camba	44.4	24.7	15.0	1.65	.41	1.8	1.8	0.8	0.0	2.0
Morado	35.1	20.4	11.3	1.80	.47	1.7	1.5	0.5	0.0	2.0
Perola	34.2	19.8	12.7	1.56	.36	2.0	0.0	0.0	0.0	2.0
Yunqueño	43.3	23.0	15.3	1.50	.31	1.8	0.5	0.3	0.5	2.0
Pojoso Chico	39.3	23.3	15.6	1.49	.39	1.7	0.7	0.2	0.2	2.0
Cholito	41.9	22.2	14.3	1.55	.34	1.2	0.2	0.0	0.3	2.0
Cubano Dentado	45.4	25.8	17.2	1.50	.36	1.8	0.2	0.2	0.8	2.0
Cateto	35.4	22.5	14.5	1.55	.42	2.0	0.5	0.0	1.2	2.0
Pororo	25.0	15.3	8.8	1.74	.43	1.5	0.2	0.2	0.0	2.0
Coroico Blanco	39.2	23.6	16.0	1.48	.40	2.0	1.5	0.7	0.3	2.0
Coroico Amarillo	37.9	23.3	14.7	1.58	.44	2.0	2.0	1.5	0.0	2.0
Coroico	37.3	24.3	16.2	1.50	.40	2.0	2.0	1.2	0.5	1.8
Enano	27.3	15.3	10.5	1.46	.33	1.5	1.0	0.0	0.0	2.0

TABLE 10. Races of Maize of Bolivia Compared in Physiological and Genetic Characters.

Race	Days to silking	Rust	Helmintho-sporium	Pilosity Intensity	Percent Hard	Percent Medium	Percent Soft	Plant Color Sun-red	Plant Color Pur-ple	Plant Color Brown	Lem-mas	Glumes	Mid-cob	Pith	Aleu-rone	Peri-carp
Confite-Puneño	95	3.9	1.5	1.1	0	0	100	2.8	1.4	0.0	24	23	58	31	4	10
Altiplano	133	—	—	—	—	—	—	—	—	—	77	67	76	11	100	72
Patillo	102	3.2	2.3	1.3	11	0	89	2.5	0.3	0.0	33	18	64	29	0	4
Kcello	145	3.4	2.0	1.3	0	18	82	2.6	0.0	0.0	64	65	60	40	0	10
Kulli	127	2.5	1.4	1.8	0	0	100	2.0	1.4	0.0	69	64	44	32	60	44
Huilcaparu	155	3.3	3.0	2.8	0	6	94	2.9	0.2	0.1	100	100	56	30	80	40
Chake-Sara	132	4.6	1.0	2.9	3	5	92	2.8	0.1	0.8	24	20	72	24	2	0
Aysuma	120	4.8	2.8	2.4	0	8	92	2.7	0.1	0.7	98	100	52	35	0	92
Patillo Grande	141	3.8	3.0	2.6	0	4	96	3.4	0.6	0.3	66	69	48	12	2	2
Checchi	127	4.0	2.8	1.8	0	0	100	2.1	0.1	0.4	44	40	40	18	100	0
Cuzco-Huilcaparu	133	3.8	3.0	2.4	2	6	92	3.0	0.1	0.5	46	49	53	23	7	8
Paru	158	3.5	2.3	2.8	0	8	93	3.8	2.8	0.1	29	70	38	33	67	77
Chuspillu	172	4.0	3.0	2.7	0	10	95	2.5	0.1	0.0	20	23	48	14	0	8
Cuzco Boliviano	135	4.0	2.2	2.7	0	0	100	3.1	0.2	0.4	20	7	33	17	0	22
Pisankalla	123	4.2	2.7	2.6	0	13	87	2.4	0.1	0.2	20	0	83	17	0	0
Uchuquilla	124	—	—	—	—	—	—	—	—	—	70	71	73	41	0	40
Karapampa	117	—	—	—	—	—	—	—	—	—	40	55	78	66	25	33
Argentino	65	1.4	1.2	3.5	90	10	0	1.3	0.2	0.0	4	4	48	6	0	8
Niñuelo	82	1.6	1.6	2.9	70	30	0	2.7	0.0	0.0	20	30	58	22	0	7
Camba	83	2.6	2.2	3.4	90	10	0	2.6	0.0	0.0	10	0	41	0	30	5
Morado	67	1.9	1.6	3.4	73	27	0	2.8	1.6	0.0	100	100	97	77	0	100
Perola	66	1.7	1.4	3.5	81	15	4	1.7	0.0	0.0	8	11	67	4	4	2
Yunqueño	68	2.0	1.4	3.4	74	20	6	2.1	1.8	0.0	31	30	65	7	22	20
Pojoso Chico	66	1.9	1.7	3.3	70	30	0	1.9	0.0	0.0	8	16	49	8	6	4
Cholito	67	2.0	1.6	3.2	52	48	0	1.5	0.2	0.0	2	0	18	0	85	2
Cubano Dentado	64	1.1	1.0	3.8	71	26	3	2.0	0.0	0.0	0	0	57	0	0	5
Cateto	69	1.7	1.4	3.5	71	29	0	1.7	0.1	0.0	0	0	24	0	0	0
Pororo	74	3.2	1.0	3.2	33	67	0	2.7	0.0	0.0	10	5	67	5	0	10
Coroico Blanco	73	3.2	2.2	3.8	87	13	0	1.8	0.4	0.0	0	4	74	4	0	0
Coroico Amarillo	76	2.5	2.2	3.9	90	7	3	2.1	0.6	0.0	13	16	43	0	0	2
Coroico	66	3.1	2.9	3.8	90	10	0	1.9	0.5	0.0	30	41	41	11	80	30
Enano	63	2.4	2.5	2.6	10	90	0	1.2	2.1	0.0	0	0	100	0	0	0

TABLE 11. List of Collections Studied as Representative of Each Race
of Bolivian Maize.

Race	Accession Numbers of Collection
1. Confite Puneño	Type Specimens: Bov. 822, 661, 891, 882, 1002. Others: Bov. 465, 512, 675, 821, 825, 827, 828, 829, 830, 853, 890, 893, 906, 914, 937, 938, 941, 942, 986, 988, 1011, 1917, 1018, 1019, 1023, 1025, 1026.
2. Altiplano	Type Specimens: Bov. 824, 494, 730, 903. Others: Bov. 369, 480, 491, 508, 542, 663, 679, 754, 889, 905, 940, 1006, 1010, 1015, 1029.
3. Patillo	Type Specimens: Bov. 493, 823, 589, 832, 502. Others: Bov. 457, 500, 516, 564, 717.
4. Kcello	Type Specimens: Bov. 1027, 948, 325, 514, 848. Others: Bov. 304, 327, 349, 455, 485, 499, 503, 522, 533, 535, 548, 541, 578, 697, 700, 826, 838, 843, 851, 854, 863, 913, 935, 947, 1003, 1005, 1009, 1021, 1022, 1024, 1028.
5. Kulli	Type Specimens: Bov. 473, 1004, 486, 844, 734. Others: Bov. 342, 353, 383, 392, 400, 475, 504, 530, 544, 602, 610, 647, 695, 696, 708, 770, 839, 1007, 1016.
6. Huilcaparu	Type Specimens: Bov. 471, 762, 574, 685, 652. Others: Bov. 324, 329, 376, 423, 441, 463, 474, 497, 515, 539, 558, 591, 604, 605, 606, 616, 620, 622, 641, 642, 651, 658, 759, 764, 771, 768, 778, 845, 876, 924, 1008, 1054, 1078, 1090, 1097, 1134.
7. Chake-Sara	Type Specimens: Bov. 439, 520, 389, 413, 952. Others: Bov. 314, 315, 365, 387, 511.
8. Aysuma	Type Specimens: Bov. 331, 1030, 443, 936, 968. Others: Bov. 479, 1012.
9. Patillo Grande	Type Specimens: Bov. 492, 501, 649, 714, 847. Others: None.
10. Checchi	Type Specimens: Bov. 421, 308, 840, 833, 320. Others: Bov. 532, 547, 588, 715, 928, 944.
11. Paru	Type Specimens: Bov. 724, 528, 718. Others: None.
12. Chuspillu	Type Specimens: Bov. 478, 458, 883, 846, 360. Others: Bov. 305, 310, 311, 347, 432, 466, 472, 576, 601, 611, 670, 692, 742, 748, 778, 774, 783, 849, 865, 873, 887, 921, 957, 972, 1104, 1112, 1124.
13. Cuzco Boliviano	Type Specimens: Bov. 752, 482, 725, 540, 1137. Others: Bov. 307, 316, 358, 375, 393, 401, 445, 446, 449, 454, 456, 470, 487, 488, 498, 513, 519, 521, 549, 595, 608, 612, 618, 638, 668, 671, 672, 673, 674, 677, 678, 680, 682, 726, 729, 732, 735, 751, 765, 769, 841, 858, 872, 877, 879, 867, 885, 886, 894, 960, 963, 1092, 1102, 1113, 1141.
.4. Pisankalla	Type Specimens: Bov. 864, 344, 760, 1106, 965. Others: Bov. 321, 337, 339, 459, 613, 656, 691, 745, 763, 782, 799, 874, 878, 942, 983, 1105.
15. Uchuquilla	Type Specimens: Bov. 869, 318, 303, 954, 1132. Others: Bov. 306, 328, 334, 338, 354, 355, 357, 364, 374, 379, 384, 390, 391, 395, 397, 427, 447, 450, 453, 460, 464, 517, 534, 561, 562, 600,

TABLE 11. List of Collections Studied as Representative of Each Race of Bolivian Maize.—Continued

Race	Accession Numbers of Collection
	607, 614, 624, 633, 650, 653, 767, 791, 834, 836, 855, 866, 868, 875, 884, 901, 908, 917, 939, 955, 975, 977, 980, 989, 1013, 1055, 1093, 1100, 1101, 1103, 1104, 1086, 1129.
16. Karapampa	Type Specimens: Bov. 422, 978, 961, 966. Others: Bov. 301, 302, 323, 394, 428, 467, 483, 531, 856, 888, 956.
17. Argentino	Type Specimens: Bov. 918, 469, 920, 461, 529. Others: Bov. 359, 373, 378, 412, 429, 468, 481, 507, 518, 563, 640, 701, 702, 704, 737, 746, 761, 860, 870, 897, 899, 904, 907, 949, 950, 1094, 1096, 1110, 1140.
18. Niñuelo	Type Specimens: Bov. 1088, 451, 495. Others: None.
19. Camba	Type Specimens: Bov. 1133, 1131. Others: Bov. 415, 538, 480, 789, 861, 1120.
20. Morado	Type Specimens: Bov. 786, 740, 743, 567. Others: Bov. 402, 584, 1126.
21. Perola	Type Specimens: Bov. 711, 712, 361, 350. Others: Bov. 437, 543, 644, 699, 703, 739, 756, 790, 803, 804, 808, 929, 982.
22. Yunqueño	Type Specimens: Bov. 665, 747, 716, 362, 332. Others: Bov. 319, 371, 398, 399, 410, 430, 496, 553, 554, 559, 560, 565, 568, 625, 628, 630, 631, 636, 639, 657, 571, 773, 776, 951, 976, 1085.
23. Pojoso Chico	Type Specimens: Bov. 809, 800, 755, 749, 750. Others: Bov. 313, 340, 351, 386, 425, 436, 448, 573, 575, 689, 713, 741, 744, 772, 788, 795, 796, 797, 798, 802, 805, 810, 812, 817, 1053, 1081.
24. Cholito	Type Specimens: Bov. 705, 781, 707, 779. Others: Bov. 309, 426, 794.
25. Cubano Dentado	Type Specimens: Bov. 585, 440. Others: None.
26. Cateto	Type Specimens: Bov. 1083, 635, 815. Others: Bov. 317, 330, 335, 336, 345, 348, 370, 418, 431, 523, 777, 807, 566, 818, 910, 1041, 1080.
27. Pororo	Type Specimens: Bov. 587, 583, 806. Others: None.
28. Coroico Blanco	Type Specimens: Bov. 1045, 1048, 1034, 1062, 1082. Others: Bov. 406, 408, 409, 416, 582, 594, 787, 792, 811, 813, 814, 820, 990, 994, 1001, 1050, 1052, 1056, 1057, 1058, 1059, 1060, 1061, 1067, 1070, 1072, 1073, 1075, 1076, 1079, 1117.
29. Coroico Amarillo	Type Specimens: Bov. 1077, 405, 1000, 438, 1042. Others: Bov. 403, 420, 434, 556, 586, 592, 593, 637, 785, 775, 999, 1074, 1084.
30. Coroico	Type Specimens: Bov. 1035, 1063, 992, 1071, 1037. Others: Bov. 396, 417, 581, 784, 987, 1033, 1038, 1039, 1040, 1046, 1047, 1051, 1064, 1065, 1116, 1118, 1119, 1121, 1122, 1123, 1127, 1135, 1142.
31. Enano	Type Specimens: Bov. 1036, 1043. Others: Bov. 993, 995, 1032, 1044.

TABLE 12. Number of Collections of Each Race Which Were Studied for Various Characters.

Race	Plants	Ears				Chromo-some Knobs
		External		Internal		
		Measured	Observed	Color	Other	
Confite Puneño	4	5	36	5	3	2
Altiplano	3	4	20	4	2	3
Patillo	4	5	10	4	2	0
Kcello	5	5	36	5	3	0
Kulli	2	5	24	5	3	3
Huilcaparu	3	5	71	5	3	5
Chake-Sara	3	5	10	5	3	0
Aysuma	3	5	7	5	3	0
Patillo Grande	3	5	5	5	3	0
Checchi	3	5	11	5	3	5
Cuzco-Huilcaparu	9	10	45	10	6	0
Paru	3	3	3	3	3	3
Chuspillu	3	5	32	5	3	5
Cuzco Boliviano	2	5	60	4	3	4
Pisankalla	4	5	21	5	3	5
Uchuquilla	3	5	90	5	3	5
Karapampa	3	4	16	4	3	3
Argentino	3	5	34	5	3	0
Niñuelo	3	3	3	3	3	3
Camba	2	2	8	2	2	0
Morado	3	5	7	5	3	0
Perola	3	4	17	4	3	3
Yunqueño	3	5	31	5	3	0
Pojoso Chico	3	5	30	5	3	3
Cholito	3	4	7	4	3	3
Cubano Dentado	2	2	2	2	2	0
Cateto	3	3	20	3	2	0
Pororo	2	3	3	3	3	2
Coroico Blanco	3	5	37	5	3	0
Coroico Amarillo	3	5	18	5	3	0
Coroico	3	5	28	5	3	5
Enano	1	2	6	1	1	1

TABLE 13. Races of Maize of Bolivia Compared in Characters of the Plants When Grown at Medellín or Montería [1]

Race	Adaptation to altitude	Height (cm.)		Stem Diameter (mm.)		Leaves			Ears per plant	Tillers	Height %		
		Plants	Ears	Minimum	Maximum	Length (cm.)	Width (cm.)	Venation index		Number	Tall	Med.	Short
						Medellín							
Camba	1380	202.5	141.2	24.7	27.4	101.1	10.3	2.91	1.8	0.22	34	50	16
						Montería							
Coroico Blanco	170	199.0	138.8	22.4	29.6	93.3	8.1	3.18	2.1	0.00	—	—	—
Coroico Amarillo	150	186.0	120.8	14.7	17.6	88.1	9.1	2.96	2.0	0.03	0.0	100	—
Coroico	180	208.2	143.6	21.2	23.1	96.8	9.1	2.96	2.5	0.00	0.0	—	0.0

[1] These data were not used for the descriptions; they are inserted only as a supplement.

TABLE 14. Races of Maize of Bolivia Compared in Physiological and Genetic Characters of the Plant When Grown at Medellín or Montería.[1]

Race	Days to silking	Rust	Helmintho-sporium	Pilosity				Plant Color			Number of Husks	
				Inten-sity	Per cent			Sun-Red	Purple	Brown	Total	Con-densed
					Hard	Medium	Soft					
Medellín												
Camba	94	3.4	3.6	1.2	16	0	0	1.6	0	0	10.8	2.8
Montería												
Coroico Blanco	71	3.2	2.0	2.4	3	64	33	1.7	2.1	0	11.9	3.7
Coroico Amarillo	70	2.0	2.0	2.2	7	77	16	2.1	1.6	0	12.7	3.3
Coroico	73	3.8	2.1	2.2	15	66	19	1.6	2.3	0	11.6	3.6

[1] These data were not used for the descriptions; they are inserted only as a supplement.

TABLE 15. Races of Maize of Bolivia Compared in Characters of the Tassel When Grown at Medellín or Montería [1]

Race	Length (cm.)				Best Developed Primary Branch			Number of Primary Branches		
	Peduncle	Branching portion	Central spike	Uppermost primary branch	Length (cm.)	Number of secondaries	Number of tertiaries	Total	With Secondaries	With tertiaries
Medellín										
Camba	13.1	14.4	24.2	17.4	25.7	3.29	1.01	25.0	9.65	2.30
Montería										
Coroico Blanco	17.2	20.3	15.4	14.5	27.0	3.58	0.97	29.2	9.08	1.93
Coroico Amarillo	16.5	19.2	19.3	13.5	24.8	2.70	0.23	31.0	10.1	0.47
Coroico	17.0	22.2	18.0	13.4	28.4	3.16	0.60	31.0	7.11	1.46

[1] These data were not used for the descriptions; they are inserted only as a supplement.